BIG IDEAS
MATH®
Modeling Real Life
Grades K–5

Differentiated Rich Math Tasks

BIG IDEAS LEARNING®

Erie, Pennsylvania
BigIdeasLearning.com

Credits: Akrain/iStock/Getty Images Plus; Tichaporn /Shutterstock.com
Cartoon Illustrations: MoreFrames Animation

Printed in the U.S.A.

ISBN 13: 978-1-64208-304-0

2 3 4 5 6 7 8 9 10—22 21 20 19 18

Contents

About the Differentiated

Differentiated Rich Math Tasks, written by Dr. Ron Larson and Dr. Laurie Boswell, combine music and literature with math to create interdisciplinary activities and discussions that are rich and deep!

When writing the rich math tasks, the authors referred to research by Nancy Butler. Her research shows that students benefit from tasks that are open, accessible, and provide multiple approaches to solve. When students are provided these opportunities, they gain the confidence they need to succeed. The rich math tasks in this program offer the following.

- Accessibility to all learners
- Real-life applications
- Multiple approaches and representations
- Collaboration and discussion
- Engagement, curiosity, and creativity
- Opportunities for extension

Each task has three different levels. This gives every student the opportunity to work on the same task, but at their own, individual level. Students who are struggling can experience the same content as students who need extension.

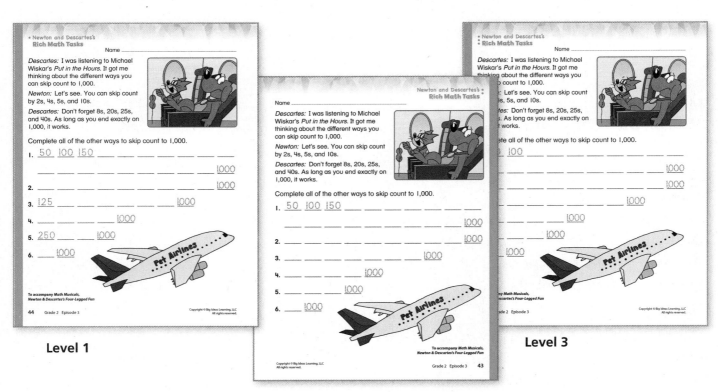

Level 1

Level 2

Level 3

Rich Math Tasks

The *Big Ideas Math Differentiated Rich Math Tasks* are directly tied to *Math Musicals Volume 1*. Newton and Descartes are featured throughout these rich and engaging tasks that ask students to make sense of and extend the ideas presented in each of the stories and songs.

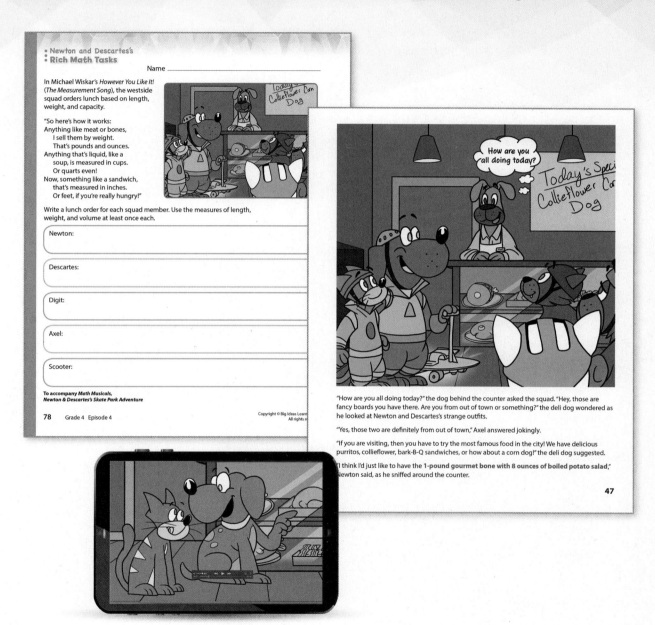

Differentiated Rich Math Tasks bring the fun of *Math Musicals* and the rigor of *Big Ideas Math* together to give every student the opportunity to succeed!

Rich Math Task
Numbers to 10

This Rich Math Task extends student learning from counting to 10 to ordering numbers to 10 and adding on. Discuss how connect-the-dot pictures are completed in order, starting at 1. Model a connect-the-dot picture of a heart on the board. Have students explain how they know the numbers are in the correct order.

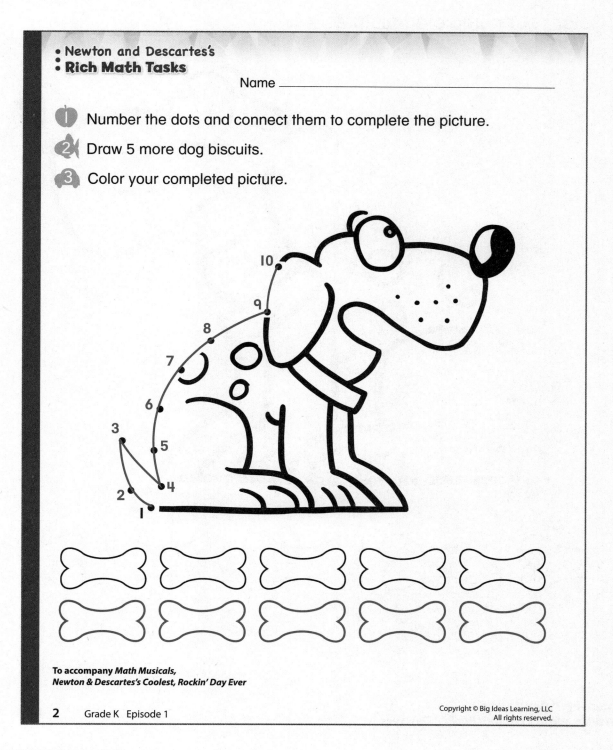

• Newton and Descartes's
• **Rich Math Tasks**

Name _____

1 Number the dots and connect them to complete the picture.

2 Draw 5 more dog biscuits.

3 Color your completed picture.

10
9
8
7
6
3
5
2
4
1

To accompany *Math Musicals,*
Newton & Descartes's Coolest, Rockin' Day Ever

Name _____

1. Number the dots and connect them to complete the picture.

2. Draw 5 more dog biscuits.

3. Color your completed picture.

Name _____

1 Number the dots and connect them to complete the picture.

2 Draw 5 more dog biscuits.

3 Color your completed picture.

To accompany *Math Musicals,*
Newton & Descartes's Coolest, Rockin' Day Ever

Name _____

1 Number the dots and connect them to complete the picture.

2 Draw 5 more dog biscuits.

3 Color your completed picture.

To accompany *Math Musicals,*
Newton & Descartes's Coolest, Rockin' Day Ever

4   Grade K   Episode 1

Rich Math Task
Partner Numbers

This Rich Math Task extends student learning from naming partner numbers to 5 to adding on. In Exercise 3, students need to understand that Newton cannot be both a player and a singer; they must use the original number of players. Discuss partner numbers for 5 and 6. Have students model the partner numbers in a number bond.

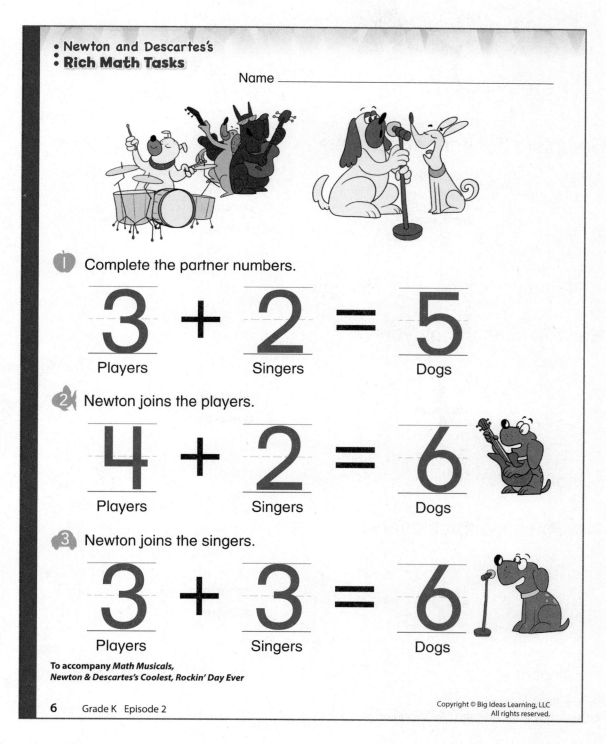

- Newton and Descartes's
- **Rich Math Tasks**

Name _____

1 Complete the partner numbers.

$$3 + 2 = 5$$

Players   Singers   Dogs

2 Newton joins the players.

$$4 + 2 = 6$$

Players   Singers   Dogs

3 Newton joins the singers.

$$3 + 3 = 6$$

Players   Singers   Dogs

To accompany *Math Musicals,*
Newton & Descartes's Coolest, Rockin' Day Ever

Name _____

1 Complete the partner numbers.

_____ **+** _____ **=** _____

Players   Singers   Dogs

2 Newton joins the players.

_____ **+** _____ **=** _____

Players   Singers   Dogs

3 Newton joins the singers.

_____ **+** _____ **=** _____

Players   Singers   Dogs

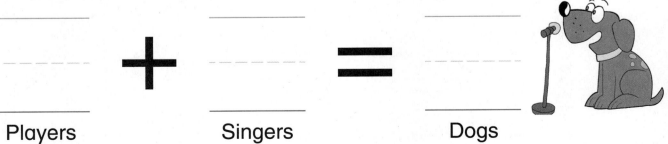

To accompany *Math Musicals,*
Newton & Descartes's Coolest, Rockin' Day Ever

Name _____

1 Complete the partner numbers.

_____   _____   _____

_ _ _ _ _   **+**   _ _ _ _ _   **=**   _ _ _ _ _

_____   _____   _____
Players   Singers   Dogs

2 Newton joins the players.

_____   _____   _____

4   **+**   _ _ _ _ _   **=**   _ _ _ _ _

_____   _____   _____
Players   Singers   Dogs

3 Newton joins the singers.

_____   _____   _____

_ _ _ _ _   **+**   _ _ _ _ _   **=**   _ _ _ _ _

_____   _____   _____
Players   Singers   Dogs

**To accompany *Math Musicals,*
*Newton & Descartes's Coolest, Rockin' Day Ever***

- **Newton and Descartes's**
Rich Math Tasks

Name _____

1 Complete the partner numbers.

_____ ✛ _____ ꞊ **5**

Players ⸻ Singers ⸻ Dogs

2 Newton joins the players.

4 ✛ _____ ꞊ _____

Players ⸻ Singers ⸻ Dogs

3 Newton joins the singers.

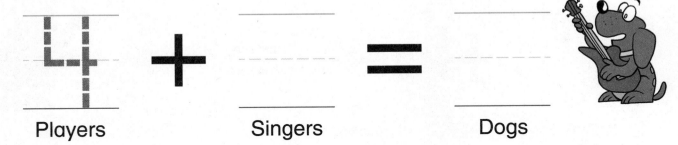

_____ ✛ _____ ꞊ **6**

Players ⸻ Singers ⸻ Dogs

To accompany *Math Musicals,*
Newton & Descartes's Coolest, Rockin' Day Ever

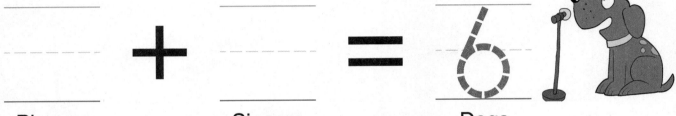

8   Grade K   Episode 2

Rich Math Task
Numbers to 20

This Rich Math Task extends student learning from counting to 20 to using ordinal numbers. Relate ordinal numbers to winners of a race. Have students identify the runners as first, second, and third. Explain how some ordinal numbers, such as *sixth*, have the number name within it.

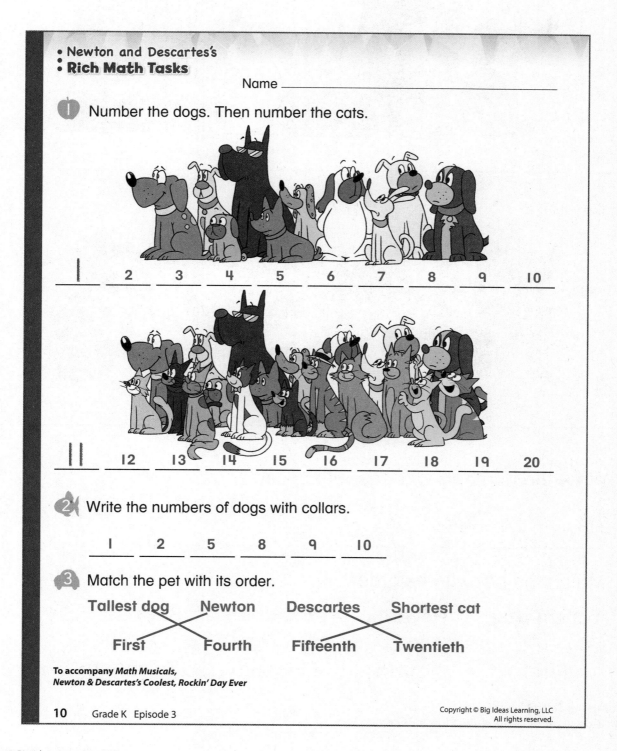

10   Grade K   Episode 3

Name _____

1 Number the dogs. Then number the cats.

_____

_____

2 Write the numbers of dogs with collars.

_____ _____ _____ _____ _____

3 Match the pet with its order.

Tallest dog   **Newton**   **Descartes**   **Shortest cat**

First   **Fourth**   **Fifteenth**   **Twentieth**

To accompany *Math Musicals,*
Newton & Descartes's Coolest, Rockin' Day Ever

Name _____

 Number the dogs. Then number the cats.

_____ _____

_____ _____

 Write the numbers of dogs with collars.

_____ _____ _____ _____ _____

 Match the pet with its order.

Tallest dog   **Newton**   **Descartes**   **Shortest cat**

First   **Fourth**   **Fifteenth**   **Twentieth**

To accompany *Math Musicals,*
Newton & Descartes's Coolest, Rockin' Day Ever

• Newton and Descartes's
Rich Math Tasks

Name _____

1 Number the dogs. Then number the cats.

I
___ ___ ___ ___ ___ ___ ___ ___ ___

II
___ ___ ___ ___ ___ ___ ___ ___ ___

2 Write the numbers of dogs with collars.

I
___ ___ ___ ___ ___

3 Match the pet with its order.

Tallest dog   Newton   Descartes   Shortest cat

First   Fourth   Fifteenth   Twentieth

To accompany *Math Musicals,*
Newton & Descartes's Coolest, Rockin' Day Ever

Rich Math Task
Shapes

This Rich Math Task extends student learning from naming attributes of two- and three-dimensional shapes to building congruent shapes. Model congruent shapes by cutting out two of the same shape and placing one on top of the other. Have students explain what they notice about the two shapes. You may want to provide cutouts of the shapes in this task.

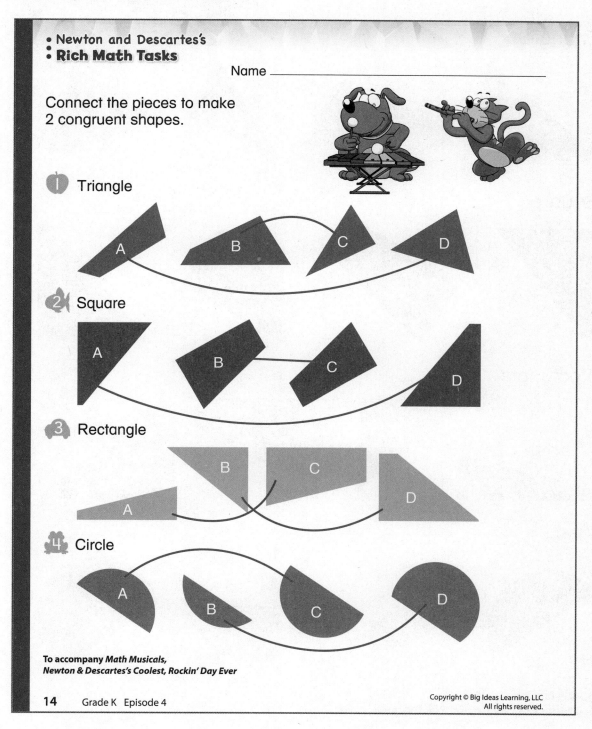

- Newton and Descartes's
- **Rich Math Tasks**

Name _____

Connect the pieces to make 2 congruent shapes.

1. Triangle

   A   B   C   D

2. Square

   A   B   C   D

3. Rectangle

   B   C   A   D

4. Circle

   A   B   C   D

To accompany *Math Musicals,*
Newton & Descartes's Coolest, Rockin' Day Ever

14   Grade K Episode 4

Name _____

Connect the pieces to make
2 congruent shapes.

1 Triangle

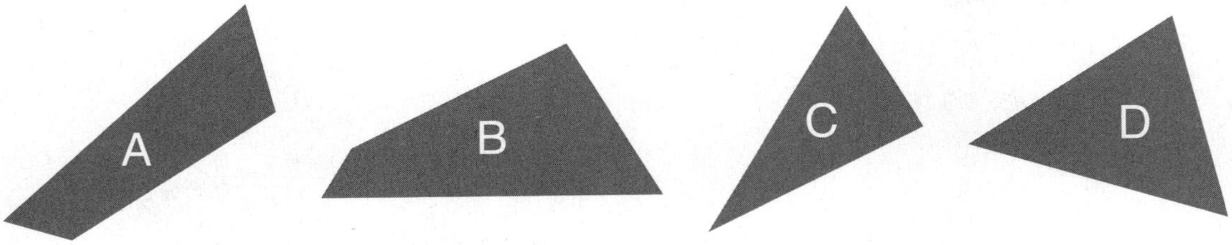

A   B   C   D

2 Square

A   B   C   D

3 Rectangle

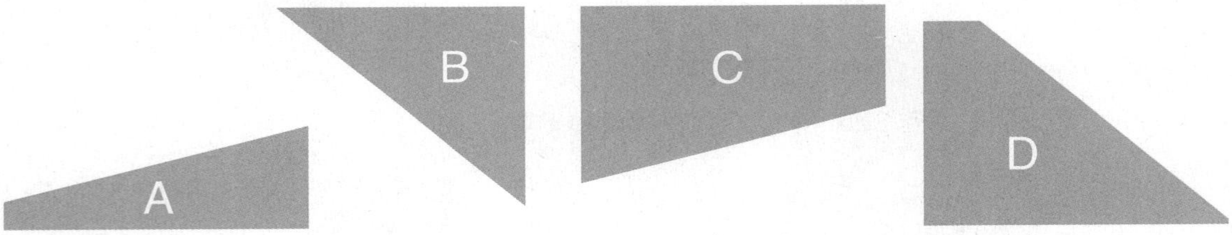

B   C   D

A

4 Circle

A   B   C   D

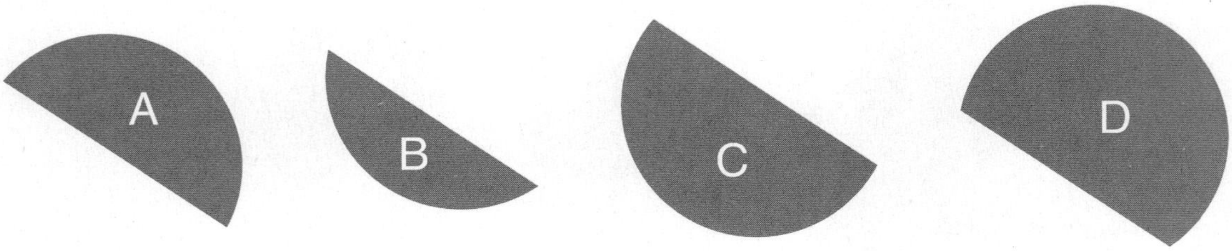

**To accompany *Math Musicals,
Newton & Descartes's Coolest, Rockin' Day Ever***

14   Grade K   Episode 4

Name _____

Connect the pieces to make
2 congruent shapes.

1 Triangle

A B C D

2 Square

A B C D

3 Rectangle

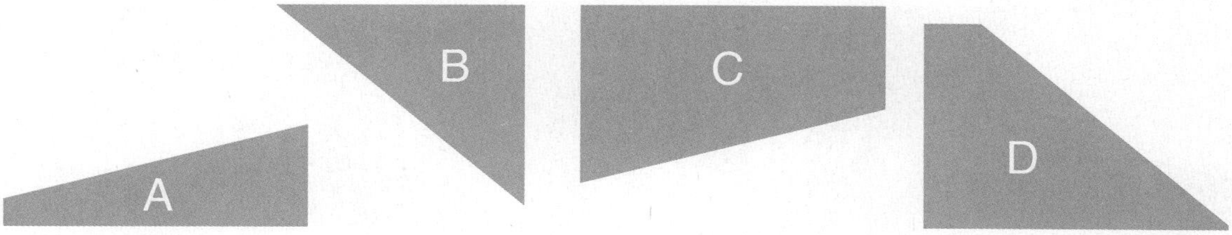

B C A D

4 Circle

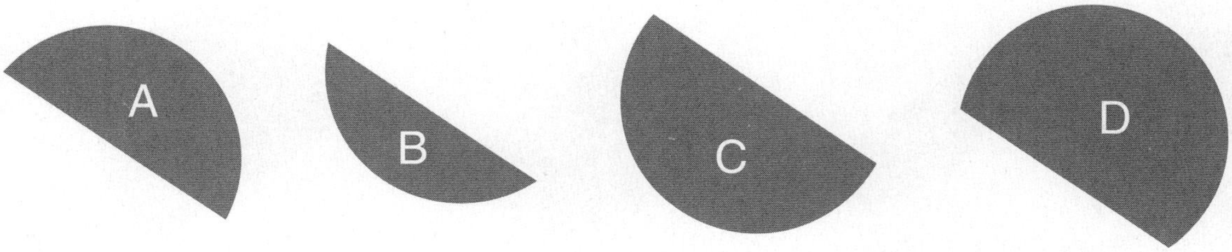

A B C D

*To accompany Math Musicals,
Newton & Descartes's Coolest, Rockin' Day Ever*

Name _____

Connect the pieces to make
2 congruent shapes.

1 Triangle

A   B   C   D

2 Square

A   B   C   D

3 Rectangle

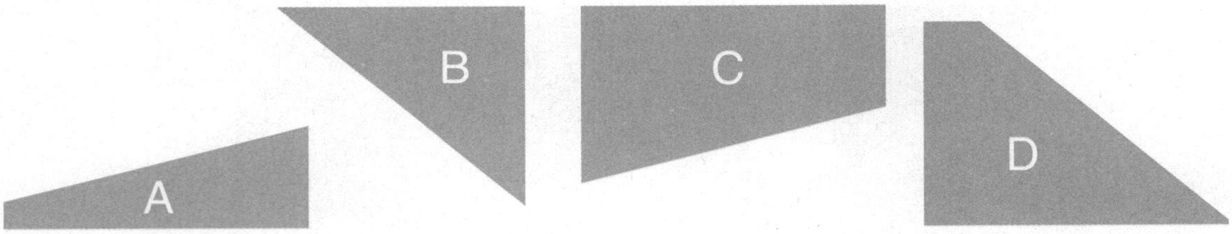

B   C   D
A

4 Circle

A   B   C   D

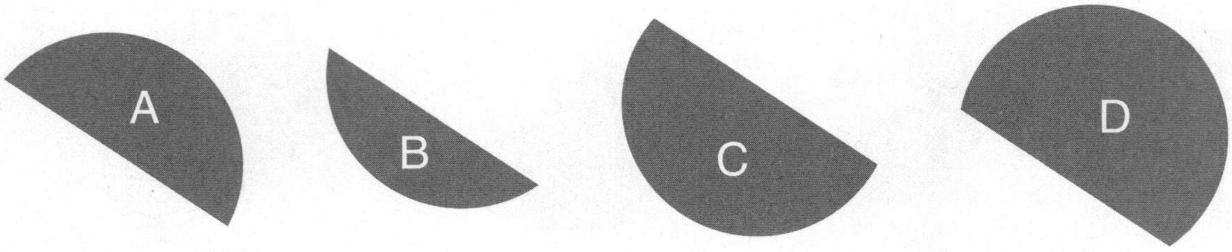

To accompany Math Musicals,
Newton & Descartes's Coolest, Rockin' Day Ever

Rich Math Task
Addition Fluency

This Rich Math Task extends student learning from adding within 10 to completing equivalent expressions. Use a pan balance and linking cubes to demonstrate that both sides of the equal sign need to equal the same amount. Have students use linking cubes to solve for the missing addends.

• Newton and Descartes's
• **Rich Math Tasks**

Name _____

Balance the equation.

1.  + __2__ = 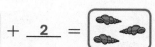 +

2. + = __0__ +

3. __3__ + = +

4. + = + __7__

5. $3 + \underline{4} = 5 + 2$

6. $3 + \underline{4} = 0 + 7$

7. $\underline{3} + 6 = 8 + 1$

8. $\underline{3} + 4 = 5 + 2$

9. $2 + 8 = \underline{7} + 3$

10. $3 + 5 = \underline{0} + 8$

11. $3 + 2 = 2 + \underline{3}$

12. $6 + 3 = 5 + \underline{4}$

13. $3 + \underline{2} + 4 = 6 + 3$

14. $3 + 2 + 4 = 6 + \underline{3}$

15. $2 + 2 + \underline{5} = 2 + 7$

16. $9 = 4 + 2 + 1 + \underline{2}$

To accompany *Math Musicals,*
Newton & Descartes's Day at the Beach

Name _____

Balance the equation.

1. 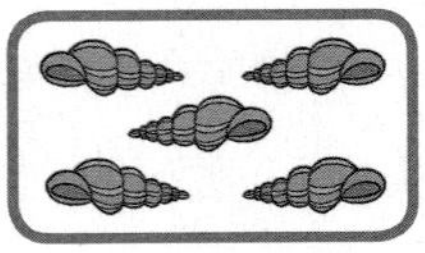 ⬚ + _____ = ⬚ + ⬚

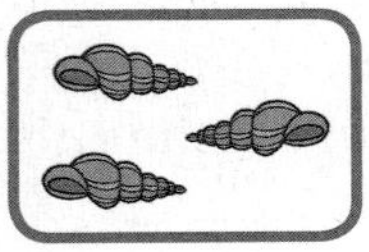

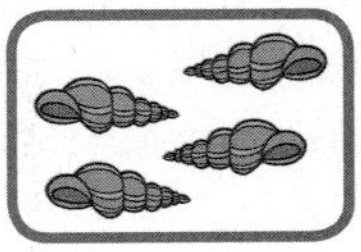

2.  ⬚ + ⬚ = _____ + ⬚

3. _____ + ⬚ = ⬚ + ⬚

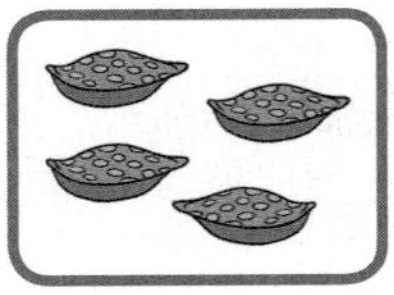

4. 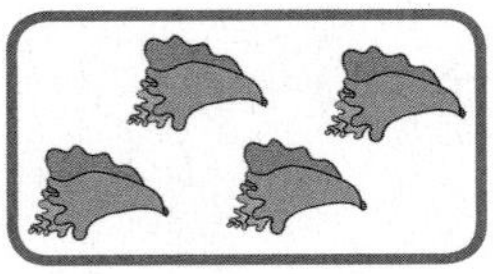 ⬚ + ⬚ = ⬚ + _____

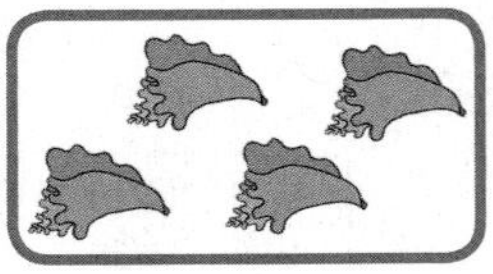

5. $3 + \underline{} = 5 + 2$

6. $3 + \underline{} = 0 + 7$

7. $\underline{} + 6 = 8 + 1$

8. $\underline{} + 4 = 5 + 2$

9. $2 + 8 = \underline{} + 3$

10. $3 + 5 = \underline{} + 8$

11. $3 + 2 = 2 + \underline{}$

12. $6 + 3 = 5 + \underline{}$

13. $3 + \underline{} + 4 = 6 + 3$

14. $3 + 2 + 4 = 6 + \underline{}$

15. $2 + 2 + \underline{} = 2 + 7$

16. $9 = 4 + 2 + 1 + \underline{}$

To accompany *Math Musicals,*
Newton & Descartes's Day at the Beach

Name _____

Balance the equation.

1. 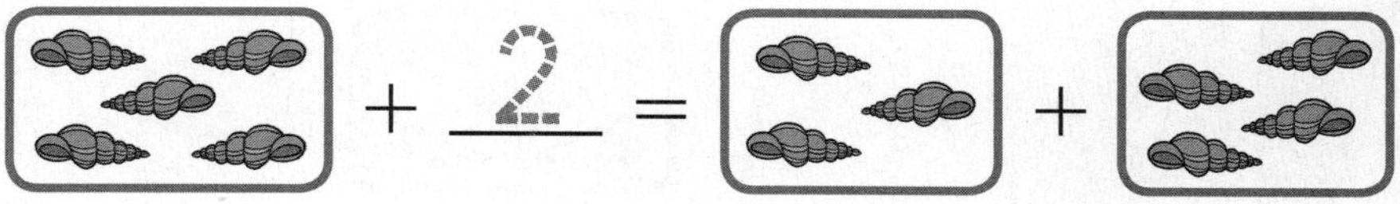 [shells] + __2__ = [shells] + [shells]

2. [shells] + [shells] = ___ + [shells]

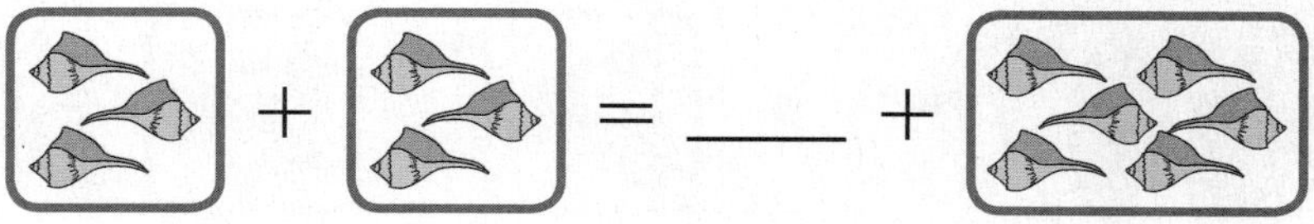

3. 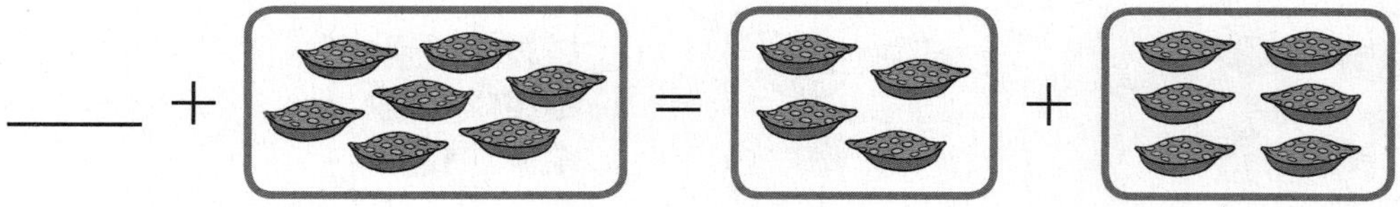 ___ + [shells] = [shells] + [shells]

4. 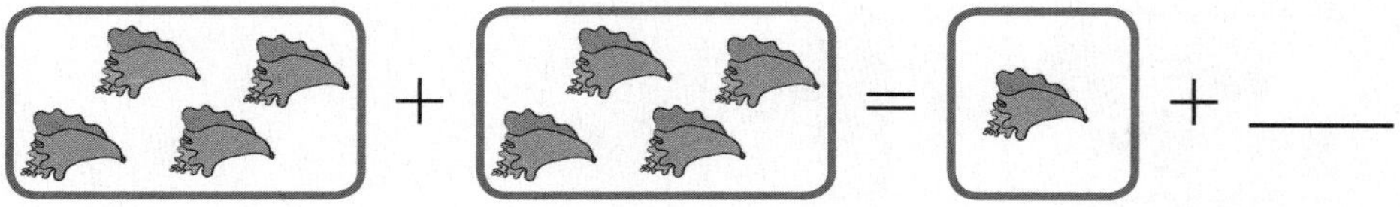 [shells] + [shells] = [shell] + ___

5. 3 + ___ = 5 + 2

6. 3 + ___ = 0 + 7

7. ___ + 6 = 8 + 1

8. ___ + 4 = 5 + 2

9. 2 + 8 = ___ + 3

10. 3 + 5 = ___ + 8

11. 3 + 2 = 2 + ___

12. 6 + 3 = 5 + ___

13. 3 + ___ + 4 = 6 + 3

14. 3 + 2 + 4 = 6 + ___

15. 2 + 2 + ___ = 2 + 7

16. 9 = 4 + 2 + 1 + ___

**To accompany *Math Musicals,
Newton & Descartes's Day at the Beach***

Name _____

Balance the equation.

1. [shells box] $+ \underline{2} = $ [shells box] $+$ [shells box]

2. [fish box] $+$ [fish box] $= \underline{\hphantom{2}} +$ [fish box]

3. $\underline{\hphantom{2}} +$ [shells box] $=$ [shells box] $+$ [shells box]

4. [fish box] $+$ [fish box] $=$ [fish box] $+ \underline{\hphantom{2}}$

5. $3 + \underline{\hphantom{2}} = 5 + 2$

6. $3 + \underline{\hphantom{2}} = 0 + 7$

7. $\underline{\hphantom{2}} + 6 = 8 + 1$

8. $\underline{3} + 4 = 5 + 2$

9. $2 + 8 = \underline{\hphantom{2}} + 3$

10. $3 + 5 = \underline{\hphantom{2}} + 8$

11. $3 + 2 = 2 + \underline{\hphantom{2}}$

12. $6 + 3 = 5 + \underline{\hphantom{2}}$

13. $3 + \underline{2} + 4 = 6 + 3$

14. $3 + 2 + 4 = 6 + \underline{\hphantom{2}}$

15. $2 + 2 + \underline{\hphantom{2}} = 2 + 7$

16. $9 = 4 + 2 + 1 + \underline{\hphantom{2}}$

To accompany *Math Musicals,*
Newton & Descartes's Day at the Beach

Rich Math Task
Addition and Subtraction Fluency

This Rich Math Task extends student learning from adding and subtracting within 10 to completing equivalent expressions using addition *and* subtraction. Use linking cubes to model the two sides of each equation.

• Newton and Descartes's
• **Rich Math Tasks**

Name _____

Balance the equation.

1. − __5__ = −

2. +  = __9__ −

3. __10__ − = −

4. − = − __1__

5. $3 + \underline{5} = 10 - 2$

6. $3 + \underline{4} = 7 - 0$

7. $\underline{10} - 6 = 5 - 1$

8. $\underline{2} + 1 = 5 - 2$

9. $8 - 4 = \underline{7} - 3$

10. $3 + 5 = 10 - \underline{2}$

11. $3 + 2 = 9 - \underline{4}$

12. $6 - 3 = 5 - \underline{2}$

13. $2 + \underline{0} + 1 = 6 - 3$

14. $1 + 2 + 4 = \underline{10} - 3$

15. $2 + 2 + \underline{1} = 7 - 2$

16. $9 = 4 + 2 + 4 - \underline{1}$

To accompany *Math Musicals,*
Newton & Descartes's Day at the Beach

Name _____

Balance the equation.

1. 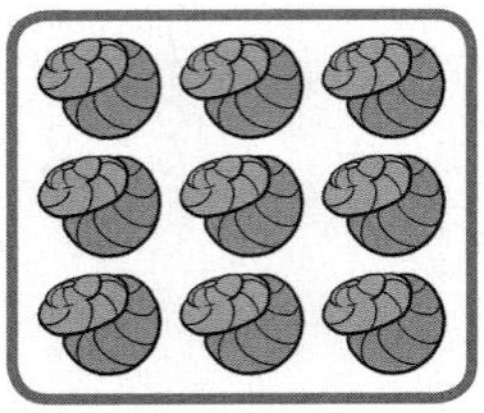  − ___ = 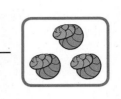 −

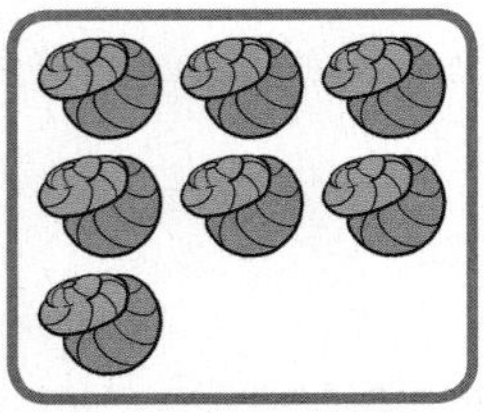

2.  + = ___ −

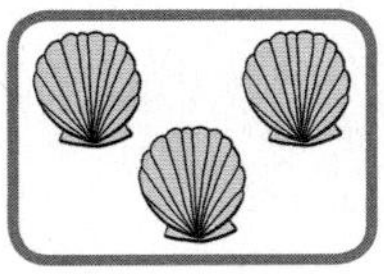

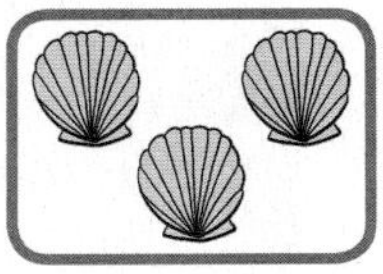

3. ___ − = −

4.  − = − ___

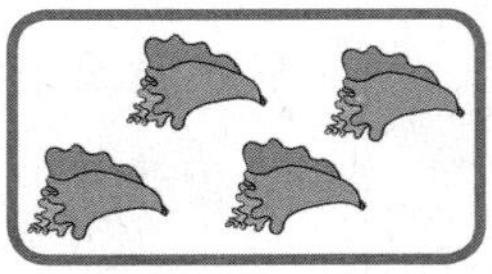

5. $3 + \underline{} = 10 - 2$

6. $3 + \underline{} = 7 - 0$

7. $\underline{} - 6 = 5 - 1$

8. $\underline{} + 1 = 5 - 2$

9. $8 - 4 = \underline{} - 3$

10. $3 + 5 = 10 - \underline{}$

11. $3 + 2 = 9 - \underline{}$

12. $6 - 3 = 5 - \underline{}$

13. $2 + \underline{} + 1 = 6 - 3$

14. $1 + 2 + 4 = \underline{} - 3$

15. $2 + 2 + \underline{} = 7 - 2$

16. $9 = 4 + 2 + 4 - \underline{}$

To accompany *Math Musicals,*
Newton & Descartes's Day at the Beach

Name _____

Balance the equation.

1. 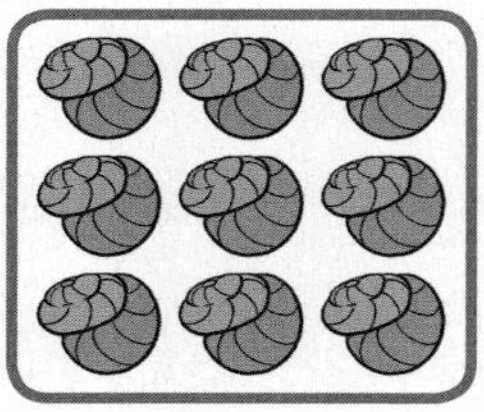  $-$ _5_ $=$ 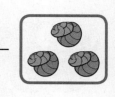 $-$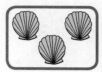

2. 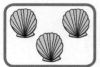 $+$  $=$ ___ $-$

3. ___ $-$  $=$  $-$

4.  $-$ ___ $=$ ___ $-$ ___

5. $3 + \underline{\hphantom{xx}} = 10 - 2$

6. $3 + \underline{\hphantom{xx}} = 7 - 0$

7. $\underline{\hphantom{xx}} - 6 = 5 - 1$

8. $\underline{\hphantom{xx}} + 1 = 5 - 2$

9. $8 - 4 = \underline{\hphantom{xx}} - 3$

10. $3 + 5 = 10 - \underline{\hphantom{xx}}$

11. $3 + 2 = 9 - \underline{\hphantom{xx}}$

12. $6 - 3 = 5 - \underline{\hphantom{xx}}$

13. $2 + \underline{\hphantom{xx}} + 1 = 6 - 3$

14. $1 + 2 + 4 = \underline{\hphantom{xx}} - 3$

15. $2 + 2 + \underline{\hphantom{xx}} = 7 - 2$

16. $9 = 4 + 2 + 4 - \underline{\hphantom{xx}}$

To accompany *Math Musicals,*
Newton & Descartes's Day at the Beach

Name _____

Balance the equation.

1. 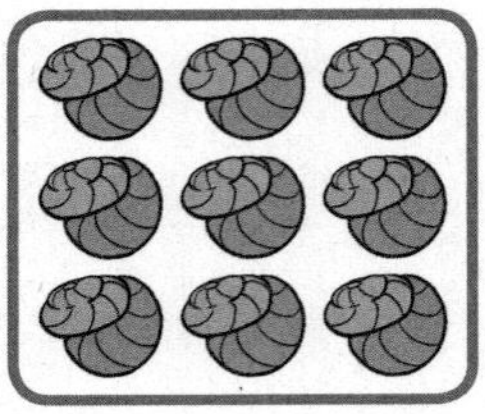 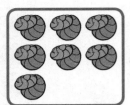 − $\underline{5}$ =

2. 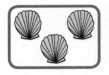 + 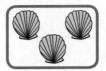 = ___ −

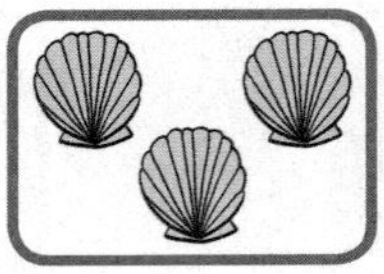

3. ___ −  =

4. ___ − ___ = ___ − ___

5. $3 + \underline{} = 10 - 2$ 6. $3 + \underline{} = 7 - 0$

7. $\underline{} - 6 = 5 - 1$ 8. $\underline{} + 1 = 5 - 2$

9. $8 - 4 = \underline{7} - 3$ 10. $3 + 5 = 10 - \underline{}$

11. $3 + 2 = 9 - \underline{}$ 12. $6 - 3 = 5 - \underline{}$

13. $2 + \underline{} + 1 = 6 - 3$ 14. $1 + 2 + 4 = \underline{} - 3$

15. $2 + 2 + \underline{1} = 7 - 2$ 16. $9 = 4 + 2 + 4 - \underline{}$

To accompany *Math Musicals,*
Newton & Descartes's Day at the Beach

Rich Math Task
Numbers to 120

This Rich Math Task extends student learning from counting and writing numbers to 120 to skip counting by tens on a number line. Model a number line on the board, counting by 1s. Discuss how number lines are similar to the 120 chart, with only one row. Ask students how the waves are similar to a number line.

• Newton and Descartes's
• **Rich Math Tasks**

Name _____

Use the code to write the word.

1. $\dfrac{C}{20}$ $\dfrac{A}{0}$ $\dfrac{K}{100}$ $\dfrac{E}{40}$

2. $\dfrac{B}{10}$ $\dfrac{E}{40}$ $\dfrac{D}{30}$

3. $\dfrac{F}{50}$ $\dfrac{A}{0}$ $\dfrac{C}{20}$ $\dfrac{E}{40}$

4. $\dfrac{D}{30}$ $\dfrac{I}{80}$ $\dfrac{G}{60}$

5. $\dfrac{H}{70}$ $\dfrac{E}{40}$ $\dfrac{A}{0}$ $\dfrac{D}{30}$

6. $\dfrac{J}{90}$ $\dfrac{A}{0}$ $\dfrac{M}{120}$

7. $\dfrac{K}{100}$ $\dfrac{I}{80}$ $\dfrac{C}{20}$ $\dfrac{K}{100}$

8. $\dfrac{A}{0}$ $\dfrac{G}{60}$ $\dfrac{E}{40}$

Use the code to write your own words.

9. ___ ___ ___ ___
   Answers will vary.
   ___ ___ ___ ___

10. ___ ___ ___
   Answers will vary.
   ___ ___ ___

To accompany *Math Musicals,*
Newton & Descartes's Day at the Beach

Name _____

Use the code to write the word.

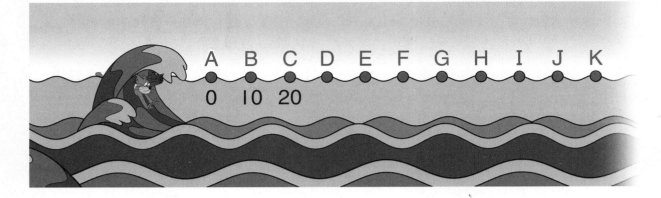

I. ___ ___ ___ ___
  20   0   100   40

2. ___ ___ ___
  10   40   30

3. ___ ___ ___ ___
  50   0   20   40

4. ___ ___ ___
  30   80   60

5. ___ ___ ___ ___
  70   40   0   30

6. ___ ___ ___
  90   0   120

7. ___ ___ ___ ___
  100   80   20   100

8. ___ ___ ___
  0   60   40

Use the code to write your own words.

9. ___ ___ ___ ___

10. ___ ___ ___

___ ___ ___ ___   ___ ___ ___

To accompany *Math Musicals,*
Newton & Descartes's Day at the Beach

Name _____

Use the code to write the word.

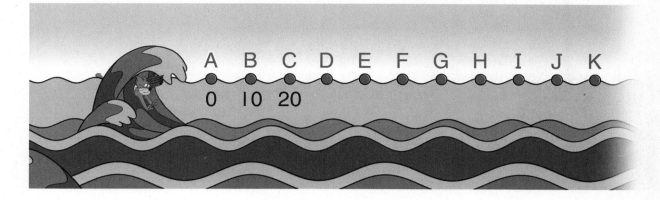

A   B   C   D   E   F   G   H   I   J   K

0   10   20

1. C   A   ___   ___
   20   0   100   40

2. ___   ___   ___
   10   40   30

3. ___   ___   ___   ___
   50   0   20   40

4. ___   ___   ___
   30   80   60

5. ___   ___   ___   ___
   70   40   0   30

6. ___   ___   ___
   90   0   120

7. ___   ___   ___   ___
   100   80   20   100

8. ___   ___   ___
   0   60   40

Use the code to write your own words.

9. ___   ___   ___   ___

   ___   ___   ___   ___

10. ___   ___   ___

    ___   ___   ___

To accompany *Math Musicals,*
Newton & Descartes's Day at the Beach

Name _____

Use the code to write the word.

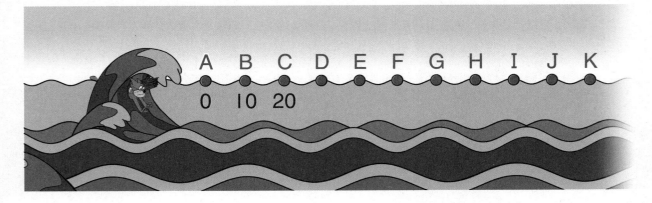

A B C D E F G H I J K

0 10 20

1. C̲ A̲ K̲ E̲

20 0 100 40

2. __ __ __

10 40 30

3. __ __ __ __

50 0 20 40

4. __ __ __

30 80 60

5. __ __ __ __

70 40 0 30

6. __ __ M̲

90 0 120

7. __ __ __ __

100 80 20 100

8. __ __ __

0 60 40

Use the code to write your own words.

9. __ __ __ __

10. __ __ __

__ __ __ __   __ __ __

To accompany Math Musicals,
Newton & Descartes's Day at the Beach

Rich Math Task
Time

This Rich Math Task extends student learning from telling time to the hour and half hour to telling time to the quarter hour. Discuss how clocks are used to tell the exact time, not just to the hour or half hour. Use a demonstration clock to model counting the minutes, by 1 or 5, focusing on the quarter hours.

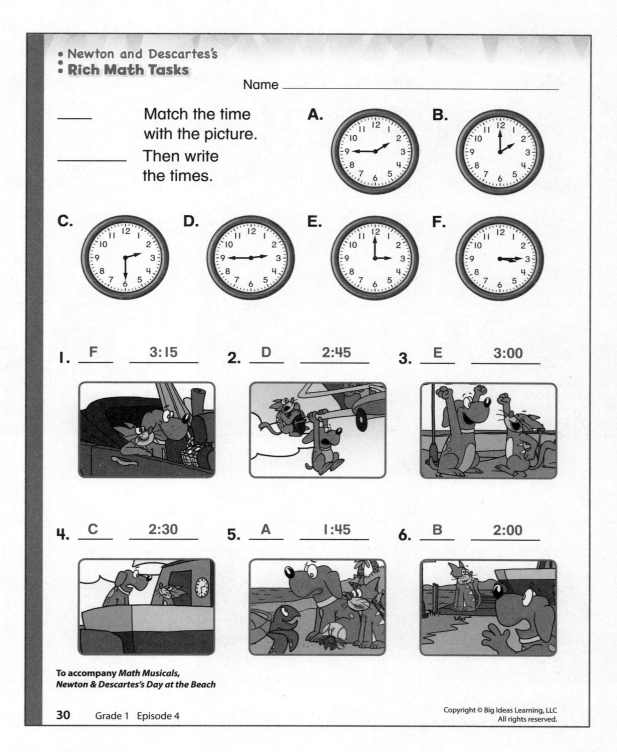

Name _____

____

Match the time
with the picture.

_____

Then write
the times.

A.

B.

C.

D.

E.

F.

I. ____ _____

2. ____ _____

3. ____ _____

4. ____ _____

5. ____ _____

6. ____ _____

To accompany *Math Musicals,*
Newton & Descartes's Day at the Beach

Name _____

____   Match the time
with the picture.

_____ Then write
the times.

A.    **B.**

C.    **D.**    **E.**    **F.**

I. _F_ ____ _____

2. ____ _____

3. ____ _____

4. ____ _____

5. ____ _____

6. ____ _____

**To accompany Math Musicals,
Newton & Descartes's Day at the Beach**

Name _____

_____ Match the time with the picture.

_____ Then write the times.

A.

B.

C.

D.

E.

F.

1. F 3:15

2. ____ ____

3. ____ ____

4. ____ ____

5. ____ ____

6. ____ ____

To accompany *Math Musicals,*
Newton & Descartes's Day at the Beach

Rich Math Task
Addition Fluency

This Rich Math Task extends student learning from adding within 100 to completing and interpreting a table using addition. Have students model addition on a rekenrek. Discuss the similarities and differences between a rekenrek and the abacus shown.

- Newton and Descartes's
- **Rich Math Tasks**

Name _____

Write Rocket and Abacus's total scores in the table.

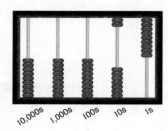

FOUR-LEGGED GAMES SCORE BOARD

Rocket	Abacus	Descartes	Newton
27 seconds	32 seconds		

Year	Rocket	Abacus	Total
1	28 sec	34 sec	62
2	31 sec	31 sec	62
3	29 sec	35 sec	64
4	30 sec	33 sec	63
5	27 sec	32 sec	59

1. Which year had the fastest total time? **Year 5**

2. Which year had the slowest total time? **Year 3**

3. Which two years had the same totals? **Year 1   Year 2**

Abacus is named after an ancient adding machine.

4. Whose score is shown on the abacus?

10,000s   1,000s   100s   10s   1s

Rocket in Year 3

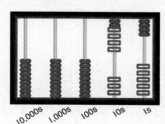

10,000s   1,000s   100s   10s   1s

5. Draw the sliding beads to show Rocket and Abacus's total score in Year 3.

To accompany *Math Musicals,*
Newton & Descartes's Four-Legged Fun

Name _____

Write Rocket and Abacus's total scores in the table.

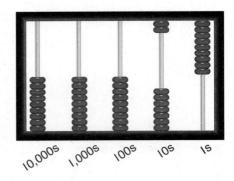

Year	Rocket	Abacus	Total
1	28 sec	34 sec	_____
2	31 sec	31 sec	_____
3	29 sec	35 sec	_____
4	30 sec	33 sec	_____
5	27 sec	32 sec	_____

1. Which year had the fastest total time? _____

2. Which year had the slowest total time? _____

3. Which two years had the same totals? _____ _____

Abacus is named after an ancient adding machine.

4. Whose score is shown on the abacus?

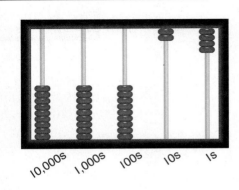

5. Draw the sliding beads to show Rocket and Abacus's total score in Year 3.

To accompany *Math Musicals,*
Newton & Descartes's Four-Legged Fun

34 Grade 2 Episode 1

Name _____

Write Rocket and Abacus's
total scores in the table.

Year	Rocket	Abacus	Total
1	28 sec	34 sec	_____
2	31 sec	31 sec	62
3	29 sec	35 sec	_____
4	30 sec	33 sec	_____
5	27 sec	32 sec	_____

FOUR-LEGGED GAMES SCORE BOARD

Rocket	Abacus	Descartes	Newton
27 seconds	32 seconds		

1. Which year had the fastest total time?   _____

2. Which year had the slowest total time?   _____

3. Which two years had the same totals?   _____   _____

Abacus is named after an ancient adding machine.

4. Whose score is shown on the abacus?

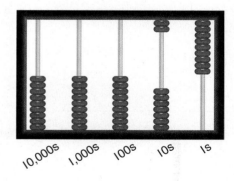

10,000s   1,000s   100s   10s   1s

5. Draw the sliding beads to show Rocket
   and Abacus's total score in Year 3.

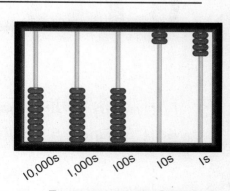

10,000s   1,000s   100s   10s   1s

**To accompany *Math Musicals,
Newton & Descartes's Four-Legged Fun***

Name _____

Write Rocket and Abacus's total scores in the table.

Year	Rocket	Abacus	Total
1	28 sec	34 sec	_____
2	31 sec	31 sec	62
3	29 sec	35 sec	_____
4	30 sec	33 sec	_____
5	27 sec	32 sec	_____

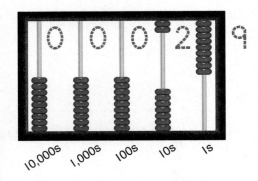

FOUR-LEGGED GAMES SCORE BOARD

Rocket	Abacus	Descartes	Newto
27 seconds	32 seconds		

1. Which year had the fastest total time?   _____

2. Which year had the slowest total time?   _____

3. Which two years had the same totals?   _____ _____

Abacus is named after an ancient adding machine.

4. Whose score is shown on the abacus?

0   0   0   2   9

10,000s   1,000s   100s   10s   1s

5. Draw the sliding beads to show Rocket and Abacus's total score in Year 3.

_____

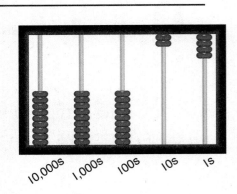

10,000s   1,000s   100s   10s   1s

To accompany Math Musicals,
Newton & Descartes's Four-Legged Fun

Rich Math Task
Subtraction

This Rich Math Task extends student learning from subtracting within 100 to completing equivalent expressions and subtracting three-digit numbers. Use a number line to discuss how subtracting three-digit numbers is similar to subtracting two-digit numbers.

Newton and Descartes's
Rich Math Tasks

Name _____

Complete the table.

FOUR-LEGGED GAMES SCORE BOARD

Rocket	Abacus	Descartes	Newton
27 seconds	32 seconds	26 seconds	29 seconds

Year	Team A	Team B	Winner
1	62 sec	64 sec	A
2	62 sec	62 sec	Tie
3	64 sec	59 sec	B
4	63 sec	64 sec	A
5	59 sec	55 sec	B

↑ Rocket & Abacus   ↑ Newton & Descartes

1. In which year was the winning team fastest?   **Year 5**

2. In which year did the winning team win by the most?   **Year 3**

Balance the equation.

3. $58 - \underline{57} = 63 - 62$

4. $58 - 58 = 63 - \underline{63}$

5. $62 - 58 = 63 - \underline{59}$

6. $68 - \underline{60} = 66 - 58$

7. $\underline{63} - 60 = 66 - 63$

8. $65 - 58 = \underline{63} - 56$

Subtract.

9.
$$\begin{array}{r} 200 \\ -\ 140 \\ \hline 60 \end{array}$$

10.
$$\begin{array}{r} 220 \\ -\ 150 \\ \hline 70 \end{array}$$

11.
$$\begin{array}{r} 120 \\ -\ 85 \\ \hline 35 \end{array}$$

12.
$$\begin{array}{r} 110 \\ -\ 65 \\ \hline 45 \end{array}$$

To accompany *Math Musicals,*
Newton & Descartes's Four-Legged Fun

38 Grade 2 Episode 2

Name _____

Complete the table.

FOUR-LEGGED GAMES SCORE BOARD

Rocket	Abacus	Descartes	Newton
27 seconds	32 seconds	26 seconds	29 seconds

Year	Team A	Team B	Winner
1	62 sec	64 sec	_____
2	62 sec	_____	Tie
3	64 sec	59 sec	_____
4	_____	64 sec	A
5	_____	_____	_____

Rocket & Abacus ↑   Newton & Descartes ↑

1. In which year was the winning team fastest? _____

2. In which year did the winning team win by the most? _____

Balance the equation.

3. $58 - \underline{\hphantom{00}} = 63 - 62$

4. $58 - 58 = 63 - \underline{\hphantom{00}}$

5. $62 - 58 = 63 - \underline{\hphantom{00}}$

6. $68 - \underline{\hphantom{00}} = 66 - 58$

7. $\underline{\hphantom{00}} - 60 = 66 - 63$

8. $65 - 58 = \underline{\hphantom{00}} - 56$

Subtract.

9.
$$\begin{array}{r} 200 \\ -\ 140 \\ \hline \end{array}$$

10.
$$\begin{array}{r} 220 \\ -\ 150 \\ \hline \end{array}$$

11.
$$\begin{array}{r} 120 \\ -\ 85 \\ \hline \end{array}$$

12.
$$\begin{array}{r} 110 \\ -\ 65 \\ \hline \end{array}$$

To accompany *Math Musicals,*
Newton & Descartes's Four-Legged Fun

Name _____

Complete the table.

FOUR-LEGGED GAMES SCORE BOARD

Rocket	Abacus	Descartes	Newton
27 seconds	32 seconds	26 seconds	29 seconds

Year	Team A	Team B	Winner
1	62 sec	64 sec	_____
2	62 sec	_62_	Tie
3	64 sec	59 sec	_____
4	_____	64 sec	A
5	_____	_____	_____

Rocket & Abacus ↑   Newton & Descartes ↑

1. In which year was the winning team fastest? _____

2. In which year did the winning team win by the most? _____

Balance the equation.

3. 58 − _____ = 63 − 62

4. 58 − 58 = 63 − _____

5. 62 − 58 = 63 − _____

6. 68 − _____ = 66 − 58

7. _____ − 60 = 66 − 63

8. 65 − 58 = _____ − 56

Subtract.

9. 200
  − 140

  _____

10. 220
  − 150

  _____

11. 120
  − 85

  _____

12. 110
  − 65

  _____

To accompany *Math Musicals,*
Newton & Descartes's Four-Legged Fun

Name _____

Complete the table.

FOUR-LEGGED GAMES SCORE BOARD

Rocket	Abacus	Descartes	Newton
27 seconds	32 seconds	26 seconds	29 seconds

Year	Team A	Team B	Winner
1	62 sec	64 sec	_____
2	62 sec	62	Tie
3	64 sec	59 sec	_____
4	_____	64 sec	A
5	_____	_____	_____

↑ Rocket & Abacus   ↑ Newton & Descartes

1. In which year was the winning team fastest? _____

2. In which year did the winning team win by the most? _____

Balance the equation.

3. 58 − 57 = 63 − 62

4. 58 − 58 = 63 − _____

5. 62 − 58 = 63 − _____

6. 68 − _____ = 66 − 58

7. _____ − 60 = 66 − 63

8. 65 − 58 = _____ − 56

Subtract.

9. 200
      − 140
      _____
       60

10. 220
       − 150
       _____

11. 120
       − 85
       _____

12. 110
       − 65
       _____

To accompany *Math Musicals,*
Newton & Descartes's Four-Legged Fun

Rich Math Task
Numbers to 1,000

This Rich Math Task extends student learning from skip counting to 1,000 by 5s, 10s, and 100s to skip counting to 1,000 by other numbers. Students will need to use the number of boxes to determine whether to increase or decrease the number used to skip count. Have students model different ways to skip count to 100. Relate counting to 1,000 to counting to 100.

• Newton and Descartes's
• **Rich Math Tasks**

Name _____

Descartes: I was listening to Michael Wiskar's *Put in the Hours*. It got me thinking about the different ways you can skip count to 1,000.

Newton: Let's see. You can skip count by 2s, 4s, 5s, and 10s.

Descartes: Don't forget 8s, 20s, 25s, and 40s. As long as you end exactly on 1,000, it works.

Complete all of the other ways to skip count to 1,000.

1. _50_ _100_ _150_ _200_ _250_ _300_ _350_ _400_ _450_ _500_

   _550_ _600_ _650_ _700_ _750_ _800_ _850_ _900_ _950_ _1,000_

2. _100_ _200_ _300_ _400_ _500_ _600_ _700_ _800_ _900_ _1,000_

3. _125_ _250_ _375_ _500_ _625_ _750_ _875_ _1,000_

4. _200_ _400_ _600_ _800_ _1,000_

5. _250_ _500_ _750_ _1,000_

6. _500_ _1,000_

To accompany *Math Musicals,*
Newton & Descartes's Four-Legged Fun

Name _____

Descartes: I was listening to Michael Wiskar's *Put in the Hours*. It got me thinking about the different ways you can skip count to 1,000.

Newton: Let's see. You can skip count by 2s, 4s, 5s, and 10s.

Descartes: Don't forget 8s, 20s, 25s, and 40s. As long as you end exactly on 1,000, it works.

Complete all of the other ways to skip count to 1,000.

1. __50__ __100__ ___ ___ ___ ___ ___ ___ ___
   ___ ___ ___ ___ ___ ___ ___ ___ __1,000__

2. ___ ___ ___ ___ ___ ___ ___ ___ ___ __1,000__

3. ___ ___ ___ ___ ___ ___ ___ __1,000__

4. ___ ___ ___ ___ __1,000__

5. ___ ___ ___ __1,000__

6. ___ __1,000__

To accompany *Math Musicals,*
Newton & Descartes's Four-Legged Fun

Name _____

Descartes: I was listening to Michael Wiskar's *Put in the Hours*. It got me thinking about the different ways you can skip count to 1,000.

Newton: Let's see. You can skip count by 2s, 4s, 5s, and 10s.

Descartes: Don't forget 8s, 20s, 25s, and 40s. As long as you end exactly on 1,000, it works.

Complete all of the other ways to skip count to 1,000.

1. _50_ _100_ _150_ ____ ____ ____ ____ ____ ____

   ____ ____ ____ ____ ____ ____ ____ ____ ____ _1,000_

2. ____ ____ ____ ____ ____ ____ ____ ____ ____ _1,000_

3. ____ ____ ____ ____ ____ ____ ____ ____ _1,000_

4. ____ ____ ____ ____ ____ _1,000_

5. ____ ____ ____ _1,000_

6. ____ ____ _1,000_

**To accompany *Math Musicals,
Newton & Descartes's Four-Legged Fun***

Name _____

Descartes: I was listening to Michael Wiskar's *Put in the Hours*. It got me thinking about the different ways you can skip count to 1,000.

Newton: Let's see. You can skip count by 2s, 4s, 5s, and 10s.

Descartes: Don't forget 8s, 20s, 25s, and 40s. As long as you end exactly on 1,000, it works.

Complete all of the other ways to skip count to 1,000.

1. __50__ __100__ __150__ ____ ____ ____ ____ ____ ____

____ ____ ____ ____ ____ ____ ____ ____ __1,000__

2. ____ ____ ____ ____ ____ ____ ____ ____ __1,000__

3. __125__ ____ ____ ____ ____ ____ ____ __1,000__

4. ____ ____ ____ ____ __1,000__

5. __250__ ____ ____ __1,000__

6. ____ __1,000__

To accompany *Math Musicals,*
Newton & Descartes's *Four-Legged Fun*

Rich Math Task
Money

This Rich Math Task extends student learning from counting money and making change to reading and writing amounts of money with a decimal point. Present currencies from other countries. Explain how different countries use different forms of currency.

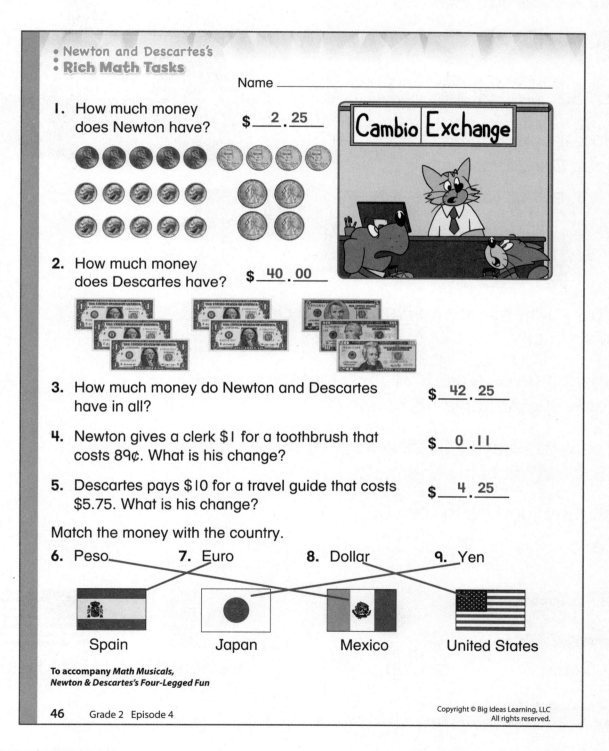

• Newton and Descartes's
• **Rich Math Tasks**

Name _____

1. How much money does Newton have? $ __2__ . __25__

2. How much money does Descartes have? $ __40__ . __00__

3. How much money do Newton and Descartes have in all? $ __42__ . __25__

4. Newton gives a clerk $1 for a toothbrush that costs 89¢. What is his change? $ __0__ . __11__

5. Descartes pays $10 for a travel guide that costs $5.75. What is his change? $ __4__ . __25__

Match the money with the country.

6. Peso   7. Euro   8. Dollar   9. Yen

Spain   Japan   Mexico   United States

To accompany *Math Musicals,*
Newton & Descartes's Four-Legged Fun

Name _____

1. How much money does Newton have? $ ___ . ___

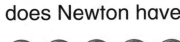

2. How much money does Descartes have? $ ___ . ___

3. How much money do Newton and Descartes have in all? $ ___ . ___

4. Newton gives a clerk $1 for a toothbrush that costs 89¢. What is his change? $ ___ . ___

5. Descartes pays $10 for a travel guide that costs $5.75. What is his change? $ ___ . ___

Match the money with the country.

6. Peso   **7.** Euro   **8.** Dollar   **9.** Yen

Spain   Japan   Mexico   United States

To accompany *Math Musicals,*
Newton & Descartes's Four-Legged Fun

Name _____

1. How much money
does Newton have? $ __2__.__25__

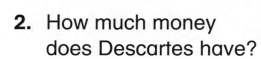

Cambio | Exchange

2. How much money
does Descartes have? $ ____.____

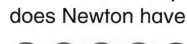

3. How much money do Newton and Descartes
have in all? $ ____.____

4. Newton gives a clerk $1 for a toothbrush that
costs 89¢. What is his change? $ ____.____

5. Descartes pays $10 for a travel guide that costs
$5.75. What is his change? $ ____.____

Match the money with the country.

6. Peso   **7.** Euro   **8.** Dollar   **9.** Yen

Spain   Japan   Mexico   United States

To accompany *Math Musicals,*
Newton & Descartes's Four-Legged Fun

Name _____

1. How much money does Newton have? $ 2.25

Cambio Exchange

2. How much money does Descartes have? $____.____

3. How much money do Newton and Descartes have in all? $____.____

4. Newton gives a clerk $1 for a toothbrush that costs 89¢. What is his change? $____.____

5. Descartes pays $10 for a travel guide that costs $5.75. What is his change? $____.____

Match the money with the country.

6. Peso **7.** Euro **8.** Dollar **9.** Yen

Spain

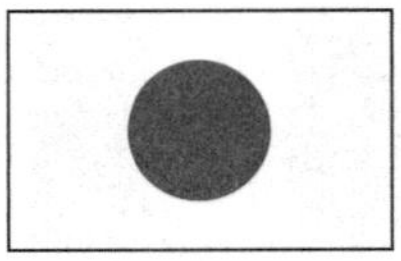

Japan

Mexico

United States

To accompany *Math Musicals,*
Newton & Descartes's Four-Legged Fun

This Rich Math Task extends student learning from multiplying by 3 to multiplying by 4, 5, and 6. Have students model the multiplication from the song, *Tiny Tapas*, to review multiplication strategies. Provide additional copies of the table to students completing multiple tables.

• Newton and Descartes's
• Rich Math Tasks

Name _____

Pérez had just ordered for himself, Newton, and Descartes, when a friend, Juan, arrived.
"Waiter, change the order for 3 people to 4 people," said Pérez.

Then, another friend, Maria, showed up.
"Hold that, waiter! Change the order from 4 people to 5 people."

Finally, a third friend, Sophia, joined the party.
"Wait! Waiter! Wait! Make that a complete order of tapas for 6 people."

Waiter! Hold that order!

5 guests: 5, 10, 15, 20, 25, 30, 35, 40
6 guests: 6, 12, 18, 24, 30, 36, 42, 48

Complete the table for 4 guests. Then copy and complete tables for 5 and 6 guests.

Guests	Type of Tapa	Tapas per Guest	Total Number of Tapas
4	Spanish Tortilla	1	4
4	Manchego Cheese	2	8
4	Cheesy Gambas	3	12
4	Cheesy Jamón	4	16
4	Cheesy Croquetas	5	20
4	Cheesy Cheese Tapas	6	24
4	Cheesy Puntillitas	7	28
4	Cheesy Olives	8	32

To accompany Math Musicals,
Newton & Descartes's Night in Madrid

Name _____

Pérez had just ordered for himself, Newton, and Descartes, when a friend, Juan, arrived.

"Waiter, change the order for 3 people to 4 people," said Pérez.

Then, another friend, Maria, showed up.

"Hold that, waiter! Change the order from 4 people to 5 people."

Finally, a third friend, Sophia, joined the party.

"Wait! Waiter! Wait! Make that a complete order of tapas for 6 people."

Complete the table for 4 guests. Then copy and complete tables for 5 and 6 guests.

Guests	Type of Tapa	Tapas per Guest	Total Number of Tapas
_____	Spanish Tortilla	1	_____
_____	Manchego Cheese	2	_____
_____	Cheesy Gambas	3	_____
_____	Cheesy Jamón	4	_____
_____	Cheesy Croquetas	5	_____
_____	Cheesy Cheese Tapas	6	_____
_____	Cheesy Puntillitas	7	_____
_____	Cheesy Olives	8	_____

To accompany Math Musicals,
Newton & Descartes's Night in Madrid

Name _____

Pérez had just ordered for himself, Newton, and Descartes, when a friend, Juan, arrived.

"Waiter, change the order for 3 people to 4 people," said Pérez.

Then, another friend, Maria, showed up.

"Hold that, waiter! Change the order from 4 people to 5 people."

Finally, a third friend, Sophia, joined the party.

"Wait! Waiter! Wait! Make that a complete order of tapas for 6 people."

Complete the table for 4 guests. Then copy and complete a table for 5 guests.

Guests	Type of Tapa	Tapas per Guest	Total Number of Tapas
4	Spanish Tortilla	1	4
4	Manchego Cheese	2	_____
4	Cheesy Gambas	3	_____
4	Cheesy Jamón	4	_____
4	Cheesy Croquetas	5	_____
4	Cheesy Cheese Tapas	6	_____
4	Cheesy Puntillitas	7	_____
4	Cheesy Olives	8	_____

**To accompany *Math Musicals,
Newton & Descartes's Night in Madrid***

Name _____

Pérez had just ordered for himself, Newton, and Descartes, when a friend, Juan, arrived. "Waiter, change the order for 3 people to 4 people," said Pérez.

Then, another friend, Maria, showed up. "Hold that, waiter! Change the order from 4 people to 5 people."

Finally, a third friend, Sophia, joined the party. "Wait! Waiter! Wait! Make that a complete order of tapas for 6 people."

Complete the table.

Guests	Type of Tapa	Tapas per Guest	Total Number of Tapas
4	Spanish Tortilla	1	4
4	Manchego Cheese	2	_____
4	Cheesy Gambas	3	_____
4	Cheesy Jamón	4	_____
4	Cheesy Croquetas	5	_____
4	Cheesy Cheese Tapas	6	_____
4	Cheesy Puntillitas	7	_____
4	Cheesy Olives	8	_____

To accompany Math Musicals,
Newton & Descartes's Night in Madrid

Rich Math Task
Multiplication Strategies

This Rich Math Task extends student learning from multiplying by 2, 3, 4, and 5 to multiplying by 6 and 7. Encourage students to write lyrics that rhyme, even though they do not have to, like in the third verse. Allow students to share their verses with the class.

· Newton and Descartes's
: Rich Math Tasks

Name _____

The song, *Olé! Olé! Olé!* (*Welcome to Spain*), by Michael Wiskar has four verses. The verses use skip counting by 2s, 3s, 4s, and 5s.

---

2 – 4 – 6 – 8

Our American friends are really great!

We go **10 – 12 – 14 – 16**

We've had our tapas
  now let's start dancing.

---

4 – 8 – 12 – 16

You my friends, are pretty nifty.

20 – 24 – 28 – 32

Now my friends, here's what we're
  going to do.

---

3 – 6 – 9 – 12

We really know how to enjoy ourselves.

We go **15 – 18 – 21 – 24**

Now it's time to hit the dance floor!

---

5 – 10 – 15 – 20

You are in a place of plenty.

25 – 30 – 35 – 40

Now it's time to start the party!

Write two more verses using skip counting by 6s and 7s.

Sample answer:

6 – 12 – __18__ – __24__

Don't leave now. Let's

  dance some more.

30 - 36 - 42 - 48

Stay and play. It's

  not that late.

Sample answer:

7 – 14 – __21__ – __28__

Come back soon.

  Let's set the date.

35 - 42 - 49 - 56

We'll dance all night.

  We'll get our kicks.

**To accompany *Math Musicals,
Newton & Descartes's Night in Madrid***

Name _____

The song, *Olé! Olé! Olé!* (*Welcome to Spain*), by Michael Wiskar has four verses. The verses use skip counting by 2s, 3s, 4s, and 5s.

2 – 4 – 6 – 8
Our American friends are really great!
We go **10 – 12 – 14 – 16**
We've had our tapas
   now let's start dancing.

4 – 8 – 12 – 16
You my friends, are pretty nifty.
20 – 24 – 28 – 32
Now my friends, here's what we're
   going to do.

3 – 6 – 9 – 12
We really know how to enjoy ourselves.
We go **15 – 18 – 21 – 24**
Now it's time to hit the dance floor!

5 – 10 – 15 – 20
You are in a place of plenty.
25 – 30 – 35 – 40
Now it's time to start the party!

Write two more verses using skip counting by 6s and 7s.

6 – 12 – _____ – _____

_____

_____

_____

_____

7 – 14 – _____ – _____

_____

_____

_____

_____

To accompany *Math Musicals,*
Newton & Descartes's Night in Madrid

54   Grade 3   Episode 2

Name _____

The song, *Olé! Olé! Olé!*
(*Welcome to Spain*), by
Michael Wiskar has four
verses. The verses use
skip counting by 2s, 3s, 4s,
and 5s.

2 – 4 – 6 – 8
Our American friends are really great!
We go **10 – 12 – 14 – 16**
We've had our tapas,
    now let's start dancing.

4 – 8 – 12 – 16
You my friends, are pretty nifty.
20 – 24 – 28 – 32
Now my friends, here's what we're
    going to do.

3 – 6 – 9 – 12
We really know how to enjoy ourselves.
We go **15 – 18 – 21 – 24**
Now it's time to hit the dance floor!

5 – 10 – 15 – 20
You are in a place of plenty.
25 – 30 – 35 – 40
Now it's time to start the party!

Write two more verses using skip counting by 6s and 7s.

6 – 12 – _____ – _____
Don't leave now. Let's
    dance some more.
_____
_____
_____

7 – 14 – _____ – _____
_____
_____
_____
_____

**To accompany *Math Musicals,
Newton & Descartes's Night in Madrid***

Name _____

The song, *Olé! Olé! Olé! (Welcome to Spain)*, by Michael Wiskar has four verses. The verses use skip counting by 2s, 3s, 4s, and 5s.

2 – 4 – 6 – 8
Our American friends are really great!
We go **10 – 12 – 14 – 16**
We've had our tapas,
    now let's start dancing.

4 – 8 – 12 – 16
You my friends, are pretty nifty.
20 – 24 – 28 – 32
Now my friends, here's what we're
    going to do.

3 – 6 – 9 – 12
We really know how to enjoy ourselves.
We go **15 – 18 – 21 – 24**
Now it's time to hit the dance floor!

5 – 10 – 15 – 20
You are in a place of plenty.
25 – 30 – 35 – 40
Now it's time to start the party!

Write two more verses using skip counting by 6s and 7s.

6 – 12 – _____ – _____
Don't leave now. Let's
    dance some more.
_____
_____
_____

7 – 14 – _____ – _____
Come back soon.
    Let's set the date.
_____
_____
_____

**To accompany *Math Musicals,
Newton & Descartes's Night in Madrid***

Rich Math Task
Fractions

This Rich Math Task extends student learning from a basic knowledge of fractions to additional denominators and equivalent fractions. Demonstrate how to use a number line or fraction strips to compare fractions. Allow students to use models to complete the task.

Newton and Descartes's
Rich Math Tasks

Name _____

The parrot was talking and talking. But, it was just a list of fractions.

Descartes wondered if the parrot was speaking in a secret code.

Use equivalent fractions and the secret code to discover what the parrot is saying.

Secret Code

$\frac{0}{1}=A$	$\frac{1}{2}=B$	$\frac{1}{3}=C$	$\frac{2}{3}=D$	$\frac{1}{4}=E$	$\frac{3}{4}=F$	$\frac{1}{5}=G$	$\frac{2}{5}=H$	$\frac{3}{5}=I$
$\frac{4}{5}=J$	$\frac{1}{6}=K$	$\frac{5}{6}=L$	$\frac{1}{7}=M$	$\frac{2}{7}=N$	$\frac{3}{7}=O$	$\frac{4}{7}=P$	$\frac{5}{7}=Q$	$\frac{6}{7}=R$
$\frac{1}{8}=S$	$\frac{3}{8}=T$	$\frac{5}{8}=U$	$\frac{7}{8}=V$	$\frac{1}{9}=W$	$\frac{2}{9}=X$	$\frac{4}{9}=Y$	$\frac{5}{9}=Z$	

$\frac{3}{5}$ $\frac{2}{12}$ $\frac{4}{14}$ $\frac{3}{7}$ $\frac{1}{9}$ $\frac{2}{18}$ $\frac{4}{10}$ $\frac{6}{10}$ $\frac{4}{6}$ $\frac{4}{10}$ $\frac{2}{5}$ $\frac{6}{14}$ $\frac{6}{16}$ $\frac{1}{4}$ $\frac{10}{12}$

 I   K   N   O   W   W   H   I   C   H   H   O   T   E   L

$\frac{4}{7}$ $\frac{9}{21}$ $\frac{10}{12}$ $\frac{10}{12}$ $\frac{8}{18}$ $\frac{9}{15}$ $\frac{2}{16}$ $\frac{2}{16}$ $\frac{6}{16}$ $\frac{0}{8}$ $\frac{4}{9}$ $\frac{6}{10}$ $\frac{2}{7}$ $\frac{2}{10}$ $\frac{0}{4}$ $\frac{6}{16}$

 P   O   L   L   Y   I   S   S   T   A   Y   I   N   G   A   T

$\frac{0}{3}$ $\frac{2}{7}$ $\frac{4}{6}$ $\frac{6}{10}$ $\frac{2}{12}$ $\frac{4}{14}$ $\frac{6}{14}$ $\frac{2}{18}$ $\frac{4}{10}$ $\frac{3}{7}$ $\frac{2}{18}$ $\frac{6}{16}$ $\frac{9}{21}$

 A   N   D   I   K   N   O   W   H   O   W   T   O

$\frac{2}{10}$ $\frac{2}{8}$ $\frac{3}{8}$ $\frac{3}{8}$ $\frac{2}{5}$ $\frac{3}{12}$ $\frac{12}{14}$ $\frac{4}{16}$

 G   E   T   T   H   E   R   E

To accompany *Math Musicals,*
Newton & Descartes's Night in Madrid

Name _____

The parrot was talking and talking. But, it was just a list of fractions.

Descartes wondered if the parrot was speaking in a secret code.

Use equivalent fractions and the secret code to discover what the parrot is saying.

Secret Code

$\frac{0}{1} = A$ $\frac{1}{2} = B$ $\frac{1}{3} = C$ $\frac{2}{3} = D$ $\frac{1}{4} = E$ $\frac{3}{4} = F$ $\frac{1}{5} = G$ $\frac{2}{5} = H$ $\frac{3}{5} = I$

$\frac{4}{5} = J$ $\frac{1}{6} = K$ $\frac{5}{6} = L$ $\frac{1}{7} = M$ $\frac{2}{7} = N$ $\frac{3}{7} = O$ $\frac{4}{7} = P$ $\frac{5}{7} = Q$ $\frac{6}{7} = R$

$\frac{1}{8} = S$ $\frac{3}{8} = T$ $\frac{5}{8} = U$ $\frac{7}{8} = V$ $\frac{1}{9} = W$ $\frac{2}{9} = X$ $\frac{4}{9} = Y$ $\frac{5}{9} = Z$

$\frac{3}{5}$ $\frac{2}{12}$ $\frac{4}{14}$ $\frac{3}{7}$ $\frac{1}{9}$ $\frac{2}{18}$ $\frac{4}{10}$ $\frac{6}{10}$ $\frac{4}{6}$ $\frac{4}{10}$ $\frac{2}{5}$ $\frac{6}{14}$ $\frac{6}{16}$ $\frac{1}{4}$ $\frac{10}{12}$

___ ___ ___ ___ ___   ___ ___ ___ ___ ___   ___ ___ ___ ___ ___

$\frac{4}{7}$ $\frac{9}{21}$ $\frac{10}{12}$ $\frac{10}{12}$ $\frac{8}{18}$ $\frac{9}{15}$ $\frac{2}{16}$ $\frac{2}{16}$ $\frac{6}{16}$ $\frac{0}{8}$ $\frac{4}{9}$ $\frac{6}{10}$ $\frac{2}{7}$ $\frac{2}{10}$ $\frac{0}{4}$ $\frac{6}{16}$

___ ___ ___ ___ ___   ___ ___   ___ ___ ___ ___ ___ ___ ___   ___ ___

$\frac{0}{3}$ $\frac{2}{7}$ $\frac{4}{6}$ $\frac{6}{10}$ $\frac{2}{12}$ $\frac{4}{14}$ $\frac{6}{14}$ $\frac{2}{18}$ $\frac{4}{10}$ $\frac{3}{7}$ $\frac{2}{18}$ $\frac{6}{16}$ $\frac{9}{21}$

___ ___ ___   ___   ___ ___ ___ ___   ___ ___ ___   ___ ___

$\frac{2}{10}$ $\frac{2}{8}$ $\frac{3}{8}$ $\frac{3}{8}$ $\frac{2}{5}$ $\frac{3}{12}$ $\frac{12}{14}$ $\frac{4}{16}$

___ ___ ___   ___ ___ ___ ___ ___

To accompany Math Musicals,
Newton & Descartes's Night in Madrid

Name _____

The parrot was talking and talking.
But, it was just a list of fractions.

Descartes wondered if the parrot
was speaking in a secret code.

Use equivalent fractions and the secret code to
discover what the parrot is saying.

Secret Code

$\frac{0}{1}$ = A $\frac{1}{2}$ = B $\frac{1}{3}$ = C $\frac{2}{3}$ = D $\frac{1}{4}$ = E $\frac{3}{4}$ = F $\frac{1}{5}$ = G $\frac{2}{5}$ = H $\frac{3}{5}$ = I

$\frac{4}{5}$ = J $\frac{1}{6}$ = K $\frac{5}{6}$ = L $\frac{1}{7}$ = M $\frac{2}{7}$ = N $\frac{3}{7}$ = O $\frac{4}{7}$ = P $\frac{5}{7}$ = Q $\frac{6}{7}$ = R

$\frac{1}{8}$ = S $\frac{3}{8}$ = T $\frac{5}{8}$ = U $\frac{7}{8}$ = V $\frac{1}{9}$ = W $\frac{2}{9}$ = X $\frac{4}{9}$ = Y $\frac{5}{9}$ = Z

$\frac{3}{5}$ $\frac{2}{12}$ $\frac{4}{14}$ $\frac{3}{7}$ $\frac{1}{9}$ $\frac{2}{18}$ $\frac{4}{10}$ $\frac{6}{10}$ $\frac{4}{6}$ $\frac{4}{10}$ $\frac{2}{5}$ $\frac{6}{14}$ $\frac{6}{16}$ $\frac{1}{4}$ $\frac{10}{12}$

 I   K   N   __   __   __   __   __   __   __   __   __   __   __   __

$\frac{4}{7}$ $\frac{9}{21}$ $\frac{10}{12}$ $\frac{10}{12}$ $\frac{8}{18}$ $\frac{9}{15}$ $\frac{2}{16}$ $\frac{2}{16}$ $\frac{6}{16}$ $\frac{0}{8}$ $\frac{4}{9}$ $\frac{6}{10}$ $\frac{2}{7}$ $\frac{2}{10}$ $\frac{0}{4}$ $\frac{6}{16}$

 __   __   __   __   __   __   __   __   __   __   __   __   __   __   __   __

$\frac{0}{3}$ $\frac{2}{7}$ $\frac{4}{6}$ $\frac{6}{10}$ $\frac{2}{12}$ $\frac{4}{14}$ $\frac{6}{14}$ $\frac{2}{18}$ $\frac{4}{10}$ $\frac{3}{7}$ $\frac{2}{18}$ $\frac{6}{16}$ $\frac{9}{21}$

 __   __   __   __   __   __   __   __   __   __   __   __   __

$\frac{2}{10}$ $\frac{2}{8}$ $\frac{3}{8}$ $\frac{3}{8}$ $\frac{2}{5}$ $\frac{3}{12}$ $\frac{12}{14}$ $\frac{4}{16}$

 __   __   __   __   __   __   __   __

**To accompany *Math Musicals,*
*Newton & Descartes's Night in Madrid***

Name _____

The parrot was talking and talking. But, it was just a list of fractions.

Descartes wondered if the parrot was speaking in a secret code.

Use equivalent fractions and the secret code to discover what the parrot is saying.

Secret Code

$\frac{0}{1}=A$	$\frac{1}{2}=B$	$\frac{1}{3}=C$	$\frac{2}{3}=D$	$\frac{1}{4}=E$	$\frac{3}{4}=F$	$\frac{1}{5}=G$	$\frac{2}{5}=H$	$\frac{3}{5}=I$
$\frac{4}{5}=J$	$\frac{1}{6}=K$	$\frac{5}{6}=L$	$\frac{1}{7}=M$	$\frac{2}{7}=N$	$\frac{3}{7}=O$	$\frac{4}{7}=P$	$\frac{5}{7}=Q$	$\frac{6}{7}=R$
$\frac{1}{8}=S$	$\frac{3}{8}=T$	$\frac{5}{8}=U$	$\frac{7}{8}=V$	$\frac{1}{9}=W$	$\frac{2}{9}=X$	$\frac{4}{9}=Y$	$\frac{5}{9}=Z$	

$\frac{3}{5}$ $\frac{2}{12}$ $\frac{4}{14}$ $\frac{3}{7}$ $\frac{1}{9}$ $\frac{2}{18}$ $\frac{4}{10}$ $\frac{6}{10}$ $\frac{4}{6}$ $\frac{4}{10}$ $\frac{2}{5}$ $\frac{6}{14}$ $\frac{6}{16}$ $\frac{1}{4}$ $\frac{10}{12}$

I   K   N   O   W   __ __ __ __ __   __ __ __ __ __

$\frac{4}{7}$ $\frac{9}{21}$ $\frac{10}{12}$ $\frac{10}{12}$ $\frac{8}{18}$ $\frac{9}{15}$ $\frac{2}{16}$ $\frac{2}{16}$ $\frac{6}{16}$ $\frac{0}{8}$ $\frac{4}{9}$ $\frac{6}{10}$ $\frac{2}{7}$ $\frac{2}{10}$ $\frac{0}{4}$ $\frac{6}{16}$

__ __ __ __ __   __ __ __   __ __ __ __ __   __ __

$\frac{0}{3}$ $\frac{2}{7}$ $\frac{4}{6}$ $\frac{6}{10}$ $\frac{2}{12}$ $\frac{4}{14}$ $\frac{6}{14}$ $\frac{2}{18}$ $\frac{4}{10}$ $\frac{3}{7}$ $\frac{2}{18}$ $\frac{6}{16}$ $\frac{9}{21}$

__ __ __ __   __ __ __ __   __ __ __ __

$\frac{2}{10}$ $\frac{2}{8}$ $\frac{3}{8}$ $\frac{3}{8}$ $\frac{2}{5}$ $\frac{3}{12}$ $\frac{12}{14}$ $\frac{4}{16}$

__ __ __ __ __ __ __ __

To accompany Math Musicals,
Newton & Descartes's Night in Madrid

Rich Math Task
Perimeter and Area

This Rich Math Task extends student learning from finding the area and perimeter of isolated rectangles to finding the area and perimeter of multiple rectangles within one larger rectangle. Discuss how area and perimeter are related. Have students explain how to find area and perimeter. Provide cover sheets for students as needed.

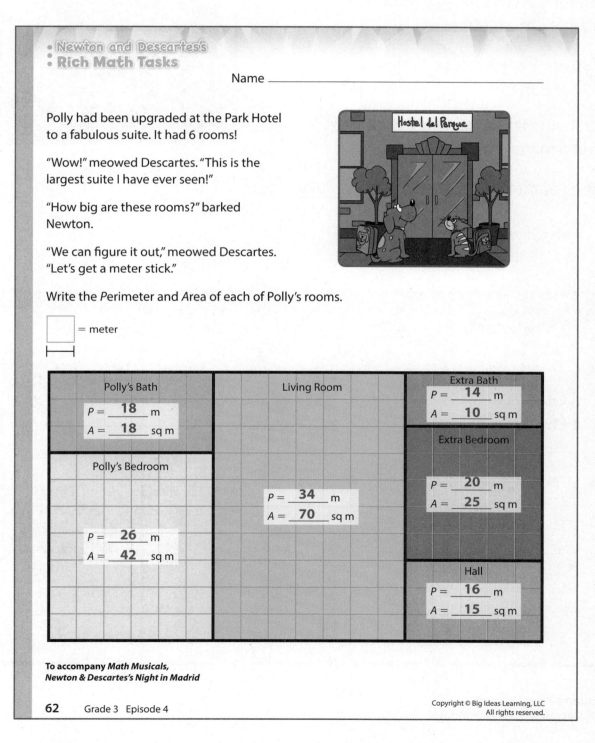

Newton and Descartes's
Rich Math Tasks

Name _____

Polly had been upgraded at the Park Hotel to a fabulous suite. It had 6 rooms!

"Wow!" meowed Descartes. "This is the largest suite I have ever seen!"

"How big are these rooms?" barked Newton.

"We can figure it out," meowed Descartes. "Let's get a meter stick."

Write the *Perimeter* and *Area* of each of Polly's rooms.

☐ = meter

├──┤

Polly's Bath	Living Room	Extra Bath
P = **18** m		P = **14** m
A = **18** sq m		A = **10** sq m

Polly's Bedroom

Extra Bedroom
P = **20** m
A = **25** sq m

Living Room:
P = **34** m
A = **70** sq m

Polly's Bedroom:
P = **26** m
A = **42** sq m

Hall
P = **16** m
A = **15** sq m

To accompany Math Musicals,
Newton & Descartes's Night in Madrid

Name _____

Polly had been upgraded at the Park Hotel to a fabulous suite. It had 6 rooms!

"Wow!" meowed Descartes. "This is the largest suite I have ever seen!"

"How big are these rooms?" barked Newton.

"We can figure it out," meowed Descartes. "Let's get a meter stick."

Write the *Perimeter* and *Area* of each of Polly's rooms.

☐ = meter

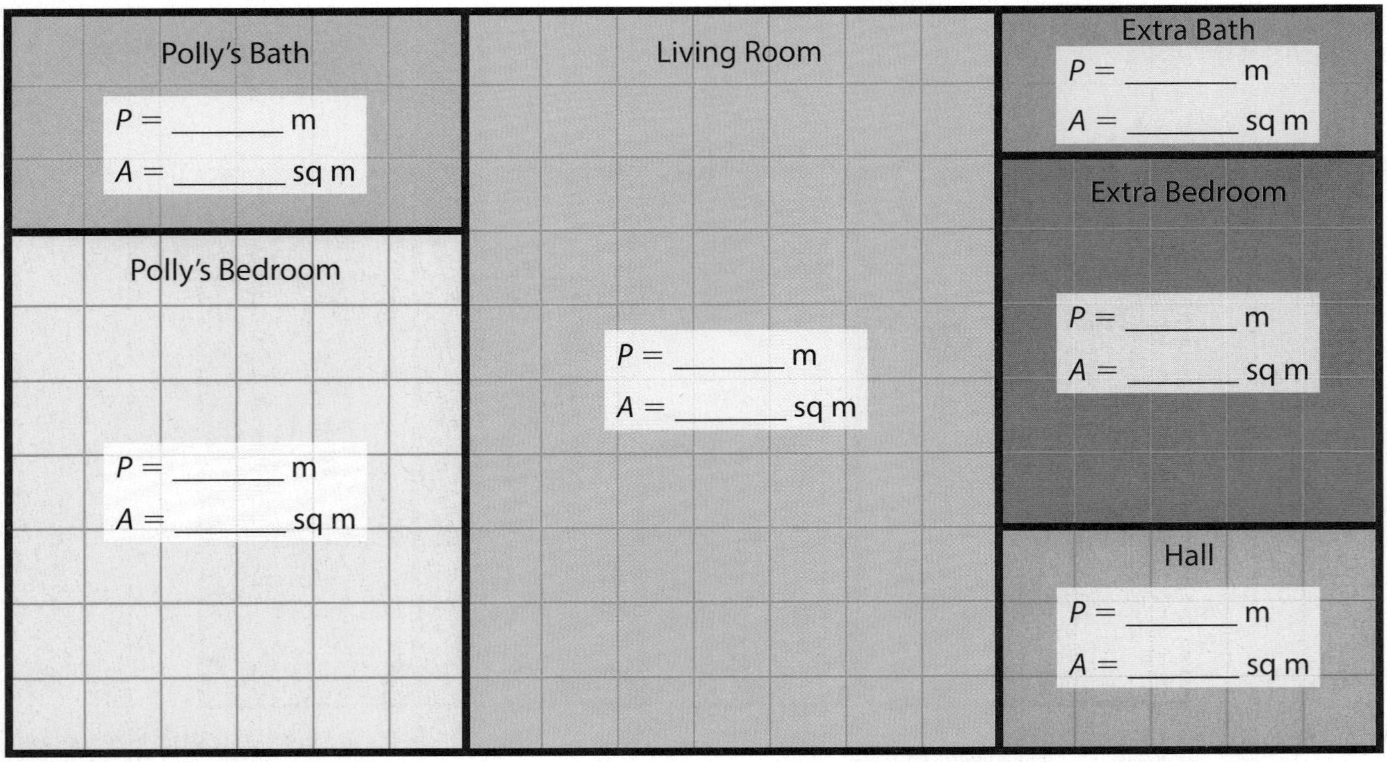

Polly's Bath	Living Room	Extra Bath
P = _____ m		P = _____ m
A = _____ sq m		A = _____ sq m
Polly's Bedroom		**Extra Bedroom**
	P = _____ m	P = _____ m
	A = _____ sq m	A = _____ sq m
P = _____ m		
A = _____ sq m		**Hall**
		P = _____ m
		A = _____ sq m

To accompany *Math Musicals,*
Newton & Descartes's Night in Madrid

Name _____

Polly had been upgraded at the Park Hotel to a fabulous suite. It had 6 rooms!

"Wow!" meowed Descartes. "This is the largest suite I have ever seen!"

"How big are these rooms?" barked Newton.

"We can figure it out," meowed Descartes. "Let's get a meter stick."

Write the *P*erimeter and *A*rea of each of Polly's rooms.

☐ = meter

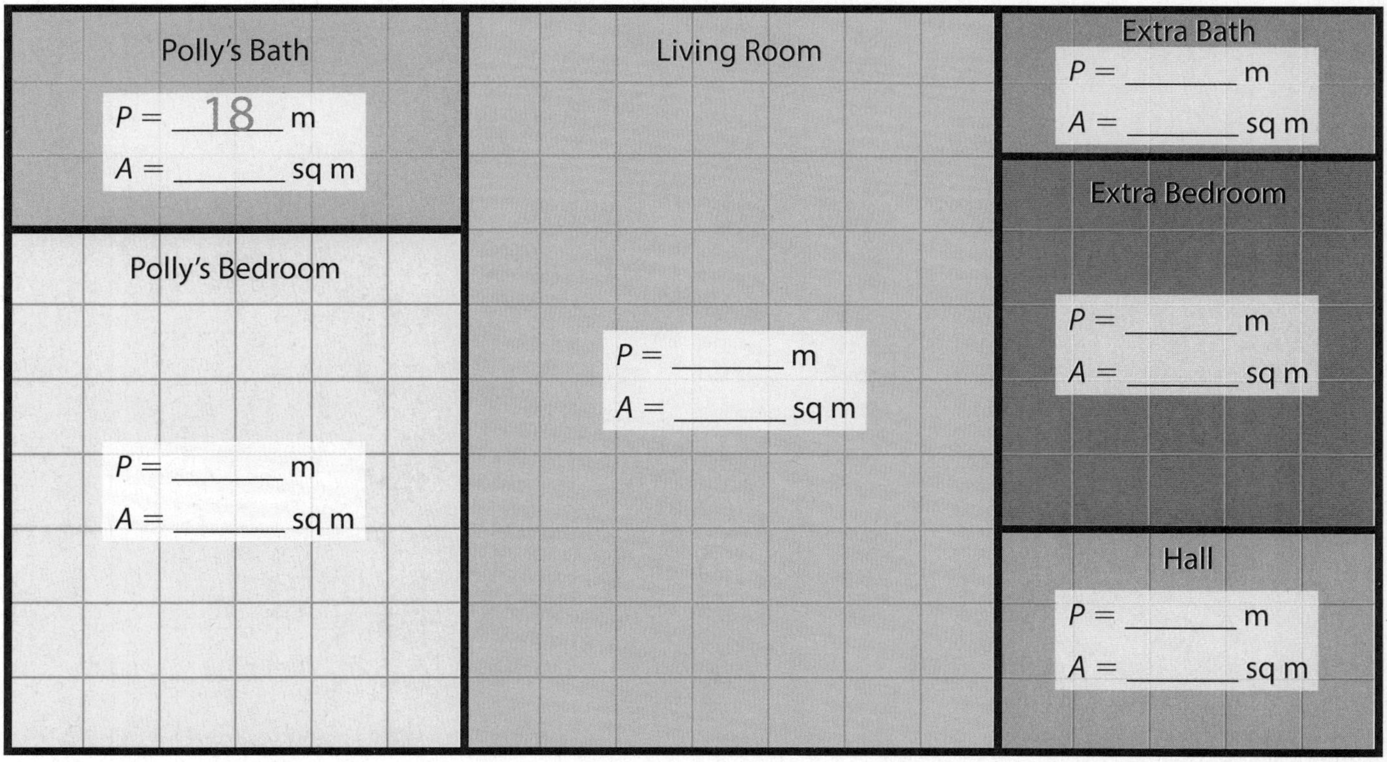

⊢——⊣

Polly's Bath	Living Room	Extra Bath
P = __18__ m		P = _____ m
A = _____ sq m		A = _____ sq m

Polly's Bedroom

P = _____ m
A = _____ sq m

Living Room

P = _____ m
A = _____ sq m

Extra Bedroom

P = _____ m
A = _____ sq m

Hall

P = _____ m
A = _____ sq m

**To accompany Math Musicals,
Newton & Descartes's Night in Madrid**

Name _____

Polly had been upgraded at the Park Hotel to a fabulous suite. It had 6 rooms!

"Wow!" meowed Descartes. "This is the largest suite I have ever seen!"

"How big are these rooms?" barked Newton.

"We can figure it out," meowed Descartes. "Let's get a meter stick."

Write the *Perimeter* and *Area* of each of Polly's rooms.

☐ = meter

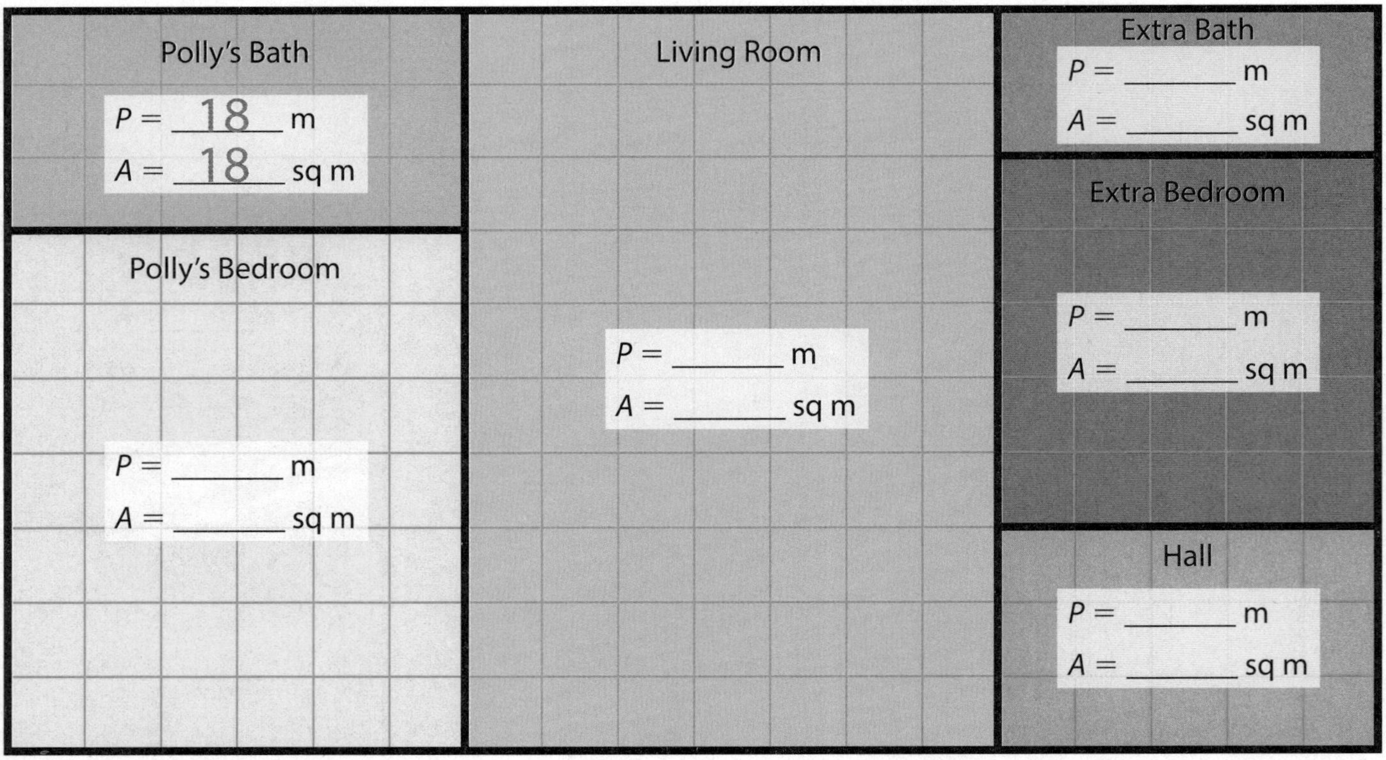

Polly's Bath	Living Room	Extra Bath
P = __18__ m		P = _____ m
A = __18__ sq m		A = _____ sq m
Polly's Bedroom		**Extra Bedroom**
		P = _____ m
		A = _____ sq m
P = _____ m	P = _____ m	
A = _____ sq m	A = _____ sq m	**Hall**
		P = _____ m
		A = _____ sq m

To accompany *Math Musicals*,
Newton & Descartes's Night in Madrid

Rich Math Task
Estimation

This Rich Math Task extends student learning from estimating with whole numbers to estimating with decimals. Use store ads to model how costs can be written using decimals. Have students round different costs in the ad to the nearest $1 and $10.

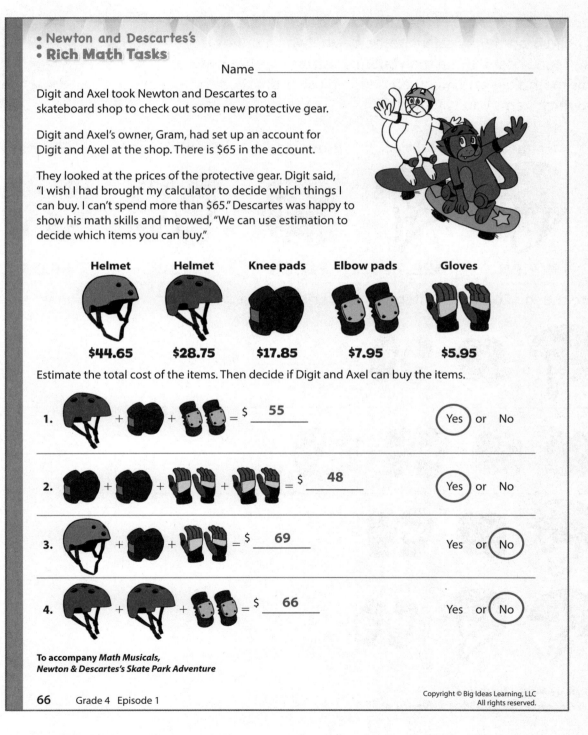

• Newton and Descartes's
• **Rich Math Tasks**

Name _____

Digit and Axel took Newton and Descartes to a skateboard shop to check out some new protective gear.

Digit and Axel's owner, Gram, had set up an account for Digit and Axel at the shop. There is $65 in the account.

They looked at the prices of the protective gear. Digit said, "I wish I had brought my calculator to decide which things I can buy. I can't spend more than $65." Descartes was happy to show his math skills and meowed, "We can use estimation to decide which items you can buy."

Helmet	Helmet	Knee pads	Elbow pads	Gloves
$44.65	$28.75	$17.85	$7.95	$5.95

Estimate the total cost of the items. Then decide if Digit and Axel can buy the items.

1. [helmet] + [knee pads] + [elbow pads] = $ __55__   (Yes) or No

2. [knee pads] + [knee pads] + [gloves] + [gloves] = $ __48__   (Yes) or No

3. [helmet] + [knee pads] + [gloves] = $ __69__   Yes or (No)

4. [helmet] + [helmet] + [elbow pads] = $ __66__   Yes or (No)

To accompany *Math Musicals*,
Newton & Descartes's Skate Park Adventure

• Newton and Descartes's
• Rich Math Tasks

Name _____

Digit and Axel took Newton and Descartes to a skateboard shop to check out some new protective gear.

Digit and Axel's owner, Gram, had set up an account for Digit and Axel at the shop. There is $65 in the account.

They looked at the prices of the protective gear. Digit said, "I wish I had brought my calculator to decide which things I can buy. I can't spend more than $65." Descartes was happy to show his math skills and meowed, "We can use estimation to decide which items you can buy."

Helmet	Helmet	Knee pads	Elbow pads	Gloves
$44.65	$28.75	$17.85	$7.95	$5.95

Estimate the total cost of the items. Then decide if Digit and Axel can buy the items.

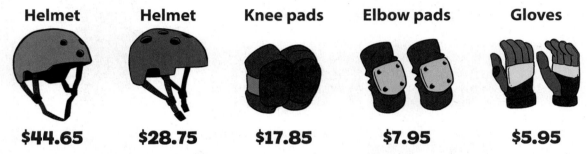

1. ▨ + ▨ + ▨ = $ _____   Yes   or   No

2. ▨ + ▨ + ▨ + ▨ = $ _____   Yes   or   No

3. ▨ + ▨ + ▨ = $ _____   Yes   or   No

4. ▨ + ▨ + ▨ = $ _____   Yes   or   No

**To accompany *Math Musicals*,
*Newton & Descartes's Skate Park Adventure***

Name _____

Digit and Axel took Newton and Descartes to a skateboard shop to check out some new protective gear.

Digit and Axel's owner, Gram, had set up an account for Digit and Axel at the shop. There is $65 in the account.

They looked at the prices of the protective gear. Digit said, "I wish I had brought my calculator to decide which things I can buy. I can't spend more than $65." Descartes was happy to show his math skills and meowed, "We can use estimation to decide which items you can buy."

Helmet	**Helmet**	**Knee pads**	**Elbow pads**	**Gloves**
$44.65	$28.75	$17.85	$7.95	$5.95

Estimate the total cost of the items. Then decide if Digit and Axel can buy the items.

1.  + ■ + ■ = $ _____   29 + 18 + 8   Yes   or   No

_____

2. ■ + ■ + ■ + ■ = $ _____   Yes   or   No

_____

3. ■ + ■ + ■ = $ _____   Yes   or   No

_____

4. ■ + ■ + ■ = $ _____   Yes   or   No

**To accompany *Math Musicals,
Newton & Descartes's Skate Park Adventure***

Name _____

Digit and Axel took Newton and Descartes to a skateboard shop to check out some new protective gear.

Digit and Axel's owner, Gram, had set up an account for Digit and Axel at the shop. There is $65 in the account.

They looked at the prices of the protective gear. Digit said, "I wish I had brought my calculator to decide which things I can buy. I can't spend more than $65." Descartes was happy to show his math skills and meowed, "We can use estimation to decide which items you can buy."

Helmet	Helmet	Knee pads	Elbow pads	Gloves
$44.65	$28.75	$17.85	$7.95	$5.95

Estimate the total cost of the items. Then decide if Digit and Axel can buy the items.

1. [helmet] + [knee pads] + [elbow pads] = $ __55__   29 + 18 + 8   Yes   or   No

2. [knee pads] + [knee pads] + [gloves] + [gloves] = $ _____   Yes   or   No

3. [helmet] + [knee pads] + [gloves] = $ _____   Yes   or   No

4. [helmet] + [helmet] + [elbow pads] = $ _____   Yes   or   No

To accompany *Math Musicals,*
Newton & Descartes's Skate Park Adventure

Rich Math Task
Divisibility

This Rich Math Task extends student learning from identifying factors and using divisibility rules to modeling all possible equal groups for a given number. Ask students to explain how they identified each set of equal groups. Ask which factor pair of 24 is *not* used and why.

Name _____

Several other cats heard about Ultra's visit and joined the crowd. Ultra surveyed the crowd and decided that she still wanted to divide the pets into groups so that each group has the same number of pets.

Ultra wants more than one group and she wants each group to have at least two pets.

Draw all of the ways the pets can be divided into groups so that there are at least two groups and at least two pets in each group. Use a circle to represent each pet.

1.

OO OO OO OO
OO OO OO OO
OO OO OO OO

2.

OOO OOO OOO
OOO OOO
OOO OOO OOO

3.

OOOO OOOO
OOOO OOOO
OOOO OOOO

4.

OOO   OOO
OOO   OOO
OOO   OOO
OOO   OOO

5.

OOOOOOOO
OOOOOOOO
OOOOOOOO

6.

OOOOOO
OOOOOO
OOOOOO
OOOOOO

To accompany Math Musicals,
Newton & Descartes's Skate Park Adventure

Name _____

Several other cats heard about Ultra's visit and joined the crowd. Ultra surveyed the crowd and decided that she still wanted to divide the pets into groups so that each group has the same number of pets.

Ultra wants more than one group and she wants each group to have at least two pets.

Draw all of the ways the pets can be divided into groups so that there are at least two groups and at least two pets in each group. Use a circle to represent each pet.

1.

2.

3.

4.

5.

6.

To accompany *Math Musicals,*
Newton & Descartes's Skate Park Adventure

Name _____

Several other cats heard about Ultra's visit and joined the crowd. Ultra surveyed the crowd and decided that she still wanted to divide the pets into groups so that each group has the same number of pets.

Ultra wants more than one group and she wants each group to have at least two pets.

Draw all of the ways the pets can be divided into groups so that there are at least two groups and at least two pets in each group. Use a circle to represent each pet.

1.

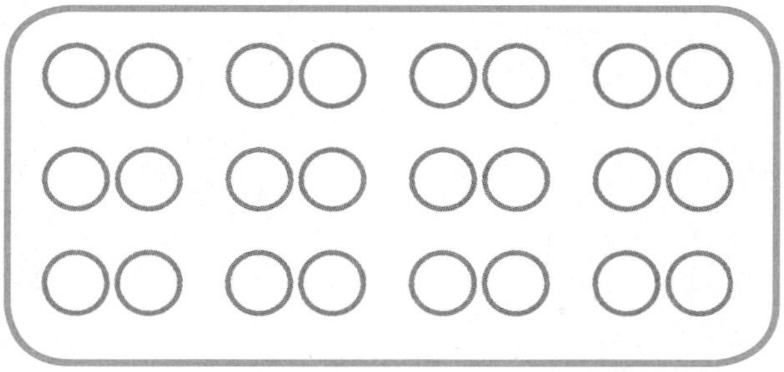

2.

3.

4.

5.

6.

To accompany *Math Musicals,*
Newton & Descartes's Skate Park Adventure

Name _____

Several other cats heard about Ultra's visit and joined the crowd. Ultra surveyed the crowd and decided that she still wanted to divide the pets into groups so that each group has the same number of pets.

Ultra wants more than one group and she wants each group to have at least two pets.

Draw all of the ways the pets can be divided into groups so that there are at least two groups and at least two pets in each group. Use a circle to represent each pet.

1.

2.

3.

4.

5.

6.

To accompany *Math Musicals,*
Newton & Descartes's Skate Park Adventure

Rich Math Task
Add and Subtract Fractions

This Rich Math Task extends student learning from adding and subtracting fractions with like denominators to adding mixed numbers and finding missing addends. Have students point to each measurement on their own body. Use fraction strips to model equivalent expressions.

- **Newton and Descartes's**
- **Rich Math Tasks**

Name _____

The dressmaker had to take Newton's measurements. This allowed the dressmaker to alter the fashion garment so that it fit Newton.

Newton's Measurements

Shoulder to elbow:	$8\frac{1}{4}$ in.
Elbow to wrist:	$8\frac{3}{4}$ in.
Half of collar:	$7\frac{3}{8}$ in.
Half of waist:	$12\frac{5}{16}$ in.
Hip to knee:	$10\frac{1}{2}$ in.
Knee to ankle:	$8\frac{1}{2}$ in.

1. How long is Newton's front leg?

2. What is Newton's neck size?

3. What is Newton's waist size?

4. How long is Newton's back leg?

$\frac{17}{}$ in.

$14\frac{3}{4}$ in.

$24\frac{5}{8}$ in.

$\frac{19}{}$ in.

Balance the equation.

5. $\frac{1}{8} + \boxed{\frac{4}{8}} = \frac{2}{8} + \frac{3}{8}$

6. $\frac{4}{6} + \frac{1}{6} = \frac{3}{6} + \boxed{\frac{2}{6}}$

7. $\boxed{\frac{2}{5}} + \frac{2}{5} = \frac{3}{5} + \frac{1}{5}$

8. $\frac{3}{10} + \frac{4}{10} = \boxed{\frac{2}{10}} + \frac{5}{10}$

9. $\frac{7}{8} - \boxed{\frac{4}{8}} = \frac{1}{8} + \frac{2}{8}$

10. $\frac{2}{5} + \frac{1}{5} = \frac{4}{5} - \boxed{\frac{1}{5}}$

To accompany Math Musicals,
Newton & Descartes's Skate Park Adventure

74   Grade 4   Episode 3

Name _____

The dressmaker had to take Newton's measurements. This allowed the dressmaker to alter the fashion garment so that it fit Newton.

Newton's Measurements

Shoulder to elbow:	$8\frac{1}{4}$ in.
Elbow to wrist:	$8\frac{3}{4}$ in.
Half of collar:	$7\frac{3}{8}$ in.
Half of waist:	$12\frac{5}{16}$ in.
Hip to knee:	$10\frac{1}{2}$ in.
Knee to ankle:	$8\frac{1}{2}$ in.

1. How long is Newton's front leg? _____ in.

2. What is Newton's neck size? _____ in.

3. What is Newton's waist size? _____ in.

4. How long is Newton's back leg? _____ in.

Balance the equation.

5. $\dfrac{1}{8} + \dfrac{\square}{\square} = \dfrac{2}{8} + \dfrac{3}{8}$

6. $\dfrac{4}{6} + \dfrac{1}{6} = \dfrac{3}{6} + \dfrac{\square}{\square}$

7. $\dfrac{\square}{\square} + \dfrac{2}{5} = \dfrac{3}{5} + \dfrac{1}{5}$

8. $\dfrac{3}{10} + \dfrac{4}{10} = \dfrac{\square}{\square} + \dfrac{5}{10}$

9. $\dfrac{7}{8} - \dfrac{\square}{\square} = \dfrac{1}{8} + \dfrac{2}{8}$

10. $\dfrac{2}{5} + \dfrac{1}{5} = \dfrac{4}{5} - \dfrac{\square}{\square}$

To accompany Math Musicals,
Newton & Descartes's Skate Park Adventure

Name _____

The dressmaker had to take Newton's measurements. This allowed the dressmaker to alter the fashion garment so that it fit Newton.

> ## Newton's Measurements
>
> Shoulder to elbow: $8\frac{1}{4}$ in.
>
> Elbow to wrist: $8\frac{3}{4}$ in.
>
> Half of collar: $7\frac{3}{8}$ in.
>
> Half of waist: $12\frac{5}{16}$ in.
>
> Hip to knee: $10\frac{1}{2}$ in.
>
> Knee to ankle: $8\frac{1}{2}$ in.

1. How long is Newton's front leg?   __17__ in.

2. What is Newton's neck size?   _____ in.

3. What is Newton's waist size?   _____ in.

4. How long is Newton's back leg?   _____ in.

Balance the equation.

5. $\dfrac{1}{8} + \dfrac{\square}{\square} = \dfrac{2}{8} + \dfrac{3}{8}$

6. $\dfrac{4}{6} + \dfrac{1}{6} = \dfrac{3}{6} + \dfrac{\square}{\square}$

7. $\dfrac{\square}{\square} + \dfrac{2}{5} = \dfrac{3}{5} + \dfrac{1}{5}$

8. $\dfrac{3}{10} + \dfrac{4}{10} = \dfrac{\square}{\square} + \dfrac{5}{10}$

9. $\dfrac{7}{8} - \dfrac{\square}{\square} = \dfrac{1}{8} + \dfrac{2}{8}$

10. $\dfrac{2}{5} + \dfrac{1}{5} = \dfrac{4}{5} - \dfrac{\square}{\square}$

To accompany *Math Musicals,*
Newton & Descartes's Skate Park Adventure

• Newton and Descartes's
Rich Math Tasks

Name _____

The dressmaker had to take Newton's measurements. This allowed the dressmaker to alter the fashion garment so that it fit Newton.

Newton's Measurements

Shoulder to elbow:	$8\frac{1}{4}$ in.
Elbow to wrist:	$8\frac{3}{4}$ in.
Half of collar:	$7\frac{3}{8}$ in.
Half of waist:	$12\frac{5}{16}$ in.
Hip to knee:	$10\frac{1}{2}$ in.
Knee to ankle:	$8\frac{1}{2}$ in.

1. How long is Newton's front leg?　　　　　　　　　__17__ in.

2. What is Newton's neck size?　　　　　　　　　_____ in.

3. What is Newton's waist size?　　　　　　　　　_____ in.

4. How long is Newton's back leg?　　　　　　　　_____ in.

Balance the equation.

5. $\dfrac{1}{8} + \dfrac{\boxed{4}}{\boxed{8}} = \dfrac{2}{8} + \dfrac{3}{8}$

6. $\dfrac{4}{6} + \dfrac{1}{6} = \dfrac{3}{6} + \dfrac{\square}{\square}$

7. $\dfrac{\square}{\square} + \dfrac{2}{5} = \dfrac{3}{5} + \dfrac{1}{5}$

8. $\dfrac{3}{10} + \dfrac{4}{10} = \dfrac{\square}{\square} + \dfrac{5}{10}$

9. $\dfrac{7}{8} - \dfrac{\square}{\square} = \dfrac{1}{8} + \dfrac{2}{8}$

10. $\dfrac{2}{5} + \dfrac{1}{5} = \dfrac{4}{5} - \dfrac{\square}{\square}$

To accompany *Math Musicals,*
Newton & Descartes's Skate Park Adventure

Rich Math Task
Equivalent Measurements

This Rich Math Task extends student learning from calculating equivalent measurements to understanding the units used for each measurement. Discuss the units used throughout the chapter and have students identify which type of measurement each unit is used for.

• Newton and Descartes's
• Rich Math Tasks

Name _____

In Michael Wiskar's *However You Like It!* (*The Measurement Song*), the westside squad orders lunch based on length, weight, and capacity.

"So here's how it works:
Anything like meat or bones,
  I sell them by weight.
  That's pounds and ounces.
Anything that's liquid, like a
  soup, is measured in cups.
  Or quarts even!
Now, something like a sandwich,
  that's measured in inches.
  Or feet, if you're really hungry!"

Write a lunch order for each squad member. Use the measures of length, weight, and volume at least once each. **Sample answers:**

Newton: **A cup of beef with barley soup and a 4-inch bone marrow sandwich**

Descartes: **6 ounces of sardine and leek salad and 2 cups of carrot juice**

Digit: **1 pint of pickerel and parsley medley and 4 ounces of kitty kibble bits**

Axel: **A 5-inch cavier sandwich on toast and a cup of soy milk**

Scooter: **A pint of warm milk poured over 4 ounces of tuna crackers**

To accompany *Math Musicals*,
Newton & Descartes's Skate Park Adventure

Name _____

In Michael Wiskar's *However You Like It!* (*The Measurement Song*), the westside squad orders lunch based on length, weight, and capacity.

"So here's how it works:
Anything like meat or bones,
    I sell them by weight.
    That's pounds and ounces.
Anything that's liquid, like a
    soup, is measured in cups.
    Or quarts even!
Now, something like a sandwich,
    that's measured in inches.
    Or feet, if you're really hungry!"

Write a lunch order for each squad member. Use the measures of length, weight, and volume at least once each.

Newton:

Descartes:

Digit:

Axel:

Scooter:

**To accompany *Math Musicals*,
*Newton & Descartes's Skate Park Adventure***

Name _____

In Michael Wiskar's *However You Like It!*
(*The Measurement Song*), the westside
squad orders lunch based on length,
weight, and capacity.

"So here's how it works:
Anything like meat or bones,
    I sell them by weight.
    That's pounds and ounces.
Anything that's liquid, like a
    soup, is measured in cups.
    Or quarts even!
Now, something like a sandwich,
    that's measured in inches.
    Or feet, if you're really hungry!"

Write a lunch order for each squad member. Use the measures of length,
weight, and volume at least once each.

Newton: A cup of beef with barley soup and a
           4-inch bone marrow sandwich

Descartes:

Digit:

Axel:

Scooter:

To accompany *Math Musicals,*
Newton & Descartes's Skate Park Adventure

Name _____

In Michael Wiskar's *However You Like It!* (*The Measurement Song*), the westside squad orders lunch based on length, weight, and capacity.

"So here's how it works:
Anything like meat or bones,
   I sell them by weight.
   That's pounds and ounces.
Anything that's liquid, like a
   soup, is measured in cups.
   Or quarts even!
Now, something like a sandwich,
   that's measured in inches.
   Or feet, if you're really hungry!"

Write a lunch order for each squad member. Use the measures of length, weight, and volume at least once each.

Newton: A cup of beef with barley soup and a 4-inch bone marrow sandwich

Descartes: 6 ounces of sardine and leek salad and 2 cups of carrot juice

Digit:

Axel:

Scooter:

To accompany *Math Musicals,*
Newton & Descartes's Skate Park Adventure

Rich Math Task
Decimals

This Rich Math Task extends student understanding of decimals to using an area model to model proportions. Have students find the area of the model shown for the 100 pound dog. Discuss how the shaded area will change for each of the other dogs.

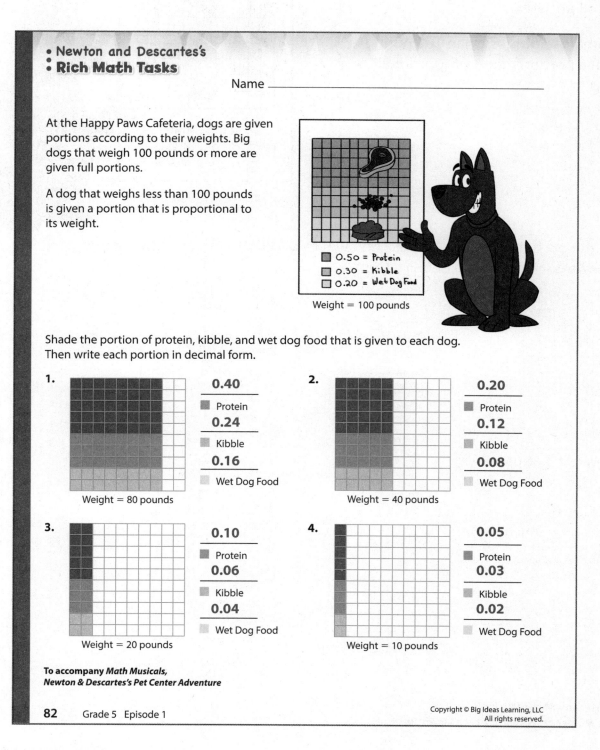

Name _____

At the Happy Paws Cafeteria, dogs are given portions according to their weights. Big dogs that weigh 100 pounds or more are given full portions.

A dog that weighs less than 100 pounds is given a portion that is proportional to its weight.

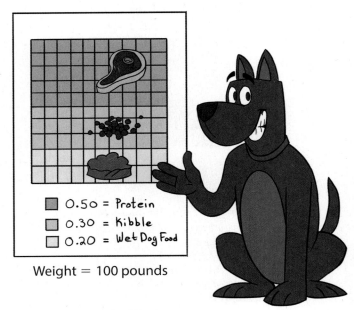

■ 0.50 = Protein
□ 0.30 = Kibble
□ 0.20 = Wet Dog Food

Weight = 100 pounds

Shade the portion of protein, kibble, and wet dog food that is given to each dog. Then write each portion in decimal form.

1.

_____ ■ Protein

_____ ▨ Kibble

_____ ▢ Wet Dog Food

Weight = 80 pounds

2.

_____ ■ Protein

_____ ▨ Kibble

_____ ▢ Wet Dog Food

Weight = 40 pounds

3.

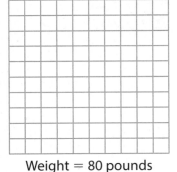

_____ ■ Protein

_____ ▨ Kibble

_____ ▢ Wet Dog Food

Weight = 20 pounds

4.

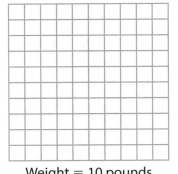

_____ ■ Protein

_____ ▨ Kibble

_____ ▢ Wet Dog Food

Weight = 10 pounds

To accompany *Math Musicals,*
Newton & Descartes's Pet Center Adventure

Name _____

At the Happy Paws Cafeteria, dogs are given portions according to their weights. Big dogs that weigh 100 pounds or more are given full portions.

A dog that weighs less than 100 pounds is given a portion that is proportional to its weight.

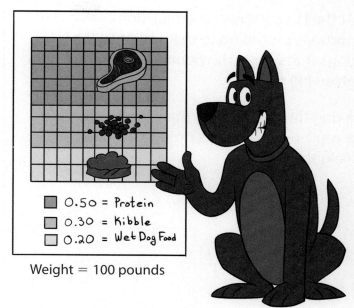

■ 0.50 = Protein
■ 0.30 = Kibble
■ 0.20 = Wet Dog Food

Weight = 100 pounds

Shade the portion of protein, kibble, and wet dog food that is given to each dog. Then write each portion in decimal form.

1.

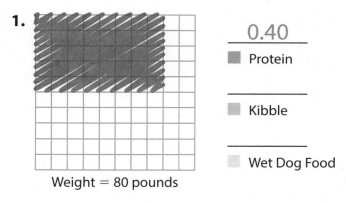

Weight = 80 pounds

0.40
■ Protein

_____
■ Kibble

_____
■ Wet Dog Food

2.

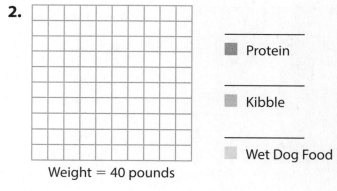

Weight = 40 pounds

_____
■ Protein

_____
■ Kibble

_____
■ Wet Dog Food

3.

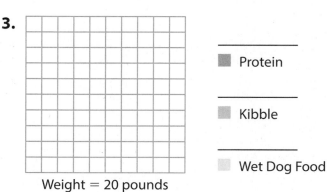

Weight = 20 pounds

_____
■ Protein

_____
■ Kibble

_____
■ Wet Dog Food

4.

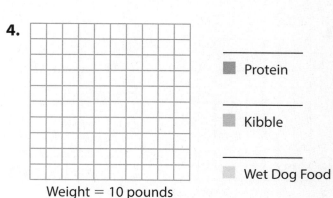

Weight = 10 pounds

_____
■ Protein

_____
■ Kibble

_____
■ Wet Dog Food

To accompany *Math Musicals,*
Newton & Descartes's Pet Center Adventure

Name _____

At the Happy Paws Cafeteria, dogs are given portions according to their weights. Big dogs that weigh 100 pounds or more are given full portions.

A dog that weighs less than 100 pounds is given a portion that is proportional to its weight.

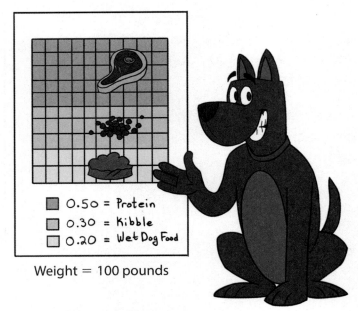

Weight = 100 pounds

0.50 = Protein
0.30 = Kibble
0.20 = Wet Dog Food

Shade the portion of protein, kibble, and wet dog food that is given to each dog. Then write each portion in decimal form.

1.

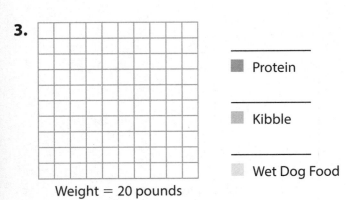

Weight = 80 pounds

0.40
■ Protein

0.24
■ Kibble

0.16
■ Wet Dog Food

2.

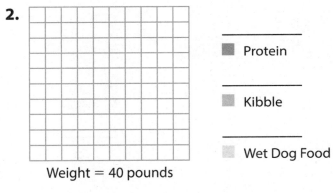

Weight = 40 pounds

_____
■ Protein

_____
■ Kibble

_____
■ Wet Dog Food

3.

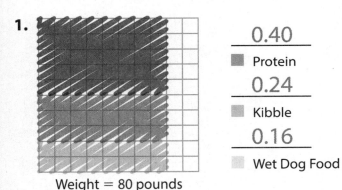

Weight = 20 pounds

_____
■ Protein

_____
■ Kibble

_____
■ Wet Dog Food

4.

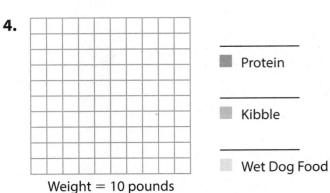

Weight = 10 pounds

_____
■ Protein

_____
■ Kibble

_____
■ Wet Dog Food

To accompany Math Musicals,
Newton & Descartes's Pet Center Adventure

Rich Math Task
Multiply Decimals

This Rich Math Task extends student learning from multiplying decimals and whole numbers to finding missing factors. Display simple equations with missing factors. Have students explain their steps for solving. Explain that, although there are decimals, the same steps are used to complete the table.

• Newton and Descartes's
• Rich Math Tasks

Name _____

Descartes was shocked as Charlie described the various monthly costs that would be charged for 6 pets at the Marbles Pet Center.

The lowest charge was $12.50 per pet per day. This covered 2 meals per day. The greatest charge was $30.75 per pet per day. This covered 3 meals and an overnight stay.

Complete the table.

Charge per Day per Pet	Days per Week	Number of Pets	Weeks per Month	Total Monthly Charge
$12.50	5	2	4	**$500.00**
$12.50	7	4	4	**$1,400.00**
$16.75	5	6	4	**$2,010.00**
$18.75	<u>5</u>	1	4	$375.00
$18.75	6	<u>6</u>	4	$2,700.00
$20.25	5	3	4	**$1,215.00**
$26.75	<u>5</u>	2	4	$1,070.00
$30.75	5	<u>3</u>	4	$1,845.00

To accompany *Math Musicals,*
Newton & Descartes's Pet Center Adventure

Name _____

Descartes was shocked as Charlie described the various monthly costs that would be charged for 6 pets at the Marbles Pet Center.

The lowest charge was $12.50 per pet per day. This covered 2 meals per day. The greatest charge was $30.75 per pet per day. This covered 3 meals and an overnight stay.

Complete the table.

Charge per Day per Pet	Days per Week	Number of Pets	Weeks per Month	Total Monthly Charge
$12.50	5	2	4	_____
$12.50	7	4	4	_____
$16.75	5	6	4	_____
$18.75	_____	1	4	$375.00
$18.75	6	_____	4	$2,700.00
$20.25	5	3	4	_____
$26.75	_____	2	4	$1,070.00
$30.75	5	_____	4	$1,845.00

To accompany *Math Musicals,*
Newton & Descartes's Pet Center Adventure

Name _____

Descartes was shocked as Charlie described the various monthly costs that would be charged for 6 pets at the Marbles Pet Center.

The lowest charge was $12.50 per pet per day. This covered 2 meals per day. The greatest charge was $30.75 per pet per day. This covered 3 meals and an overnight stay.

Complete the table.

Charge per Day per Pet	Days per Week	Number of Pets	Weeks per Month	Total Monthly Charge
$12.50	5	2	4	$500.00
$12.50	7	4	4	_____
$16.75	5	6	4	_____
$18.75	_____	1	4	$375.00
$18.75	6	_____	4	$2,700.00
$20.25	5	3	4	_____
$26.75	_____	2	4	$1,070.00
$30.75	5	_____	4	$1,845.00

**To accompany *Math Musicals*,
*Newton & Descartes's Pet Center Adventure***

• Newton and Descartes's
Rich Math Tasks

Name _____

Descartes was shocked as Charlie described the various monthly costs that would be charged for 6 pets at the Marbles Pet Center.

The lowest charge was $12.50 per pet per day. This covered 2 meals per day. The greatest charge was $30.75 per pet per day. This covered 3 meals and an overnight stay.

Complete the table.

Charge per Day per Pet	Days per Week	Number of Pets	Weeks per Month	Total Monthly Charge
$12.50	5	2	4	$500.00
$12.50	7	4	4	_____
$16.75	5	6	4	_____
$18.75	5	1	4	$375.00
$18.75	6	_____	4	$2,700.00
$20.25	5	3	4	_____
$26.75	_____	2	4	$1,070.00
$30.75	5	_____	4	$1,845.00

To accompany Math Musicals,
Newton & Descartes's Pet Center Adventure

Rich Math Task
Add and Subtract Fractions

This Rich Math Task extends student learning from adding fractions with unlike denominators to identifying missing addends. Use fraction strips to model how a whole can be made of fractions with different denominators.

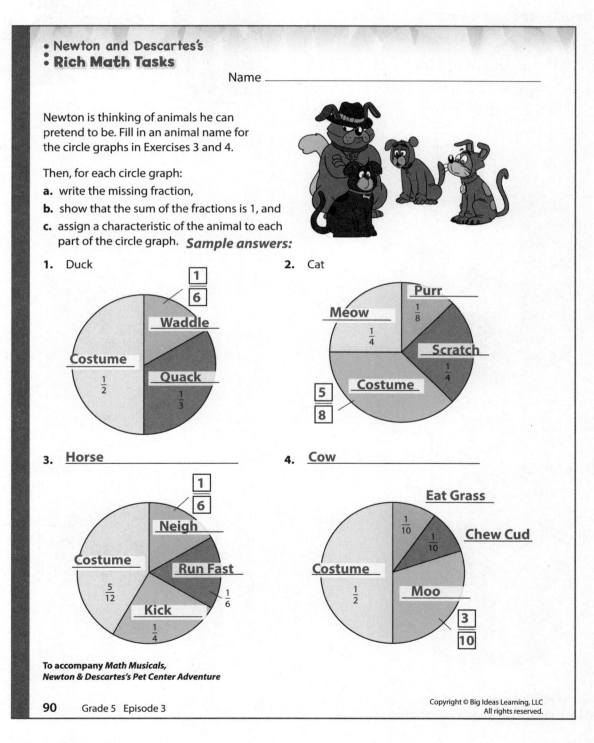

• Newton and Descartes's
• **Rich Math Tasks**

Name _____

Newton is thinking of animals he can pretend to be. Fill in an animal name for the circle graphs in Exercises 3 and 4.

Then, for each circle graph:

a. write the missing fraction,

b. show that the sum of the fractions is 1, and

c. assign a characteristic of the animal to each part of the circle graph. *Sample answers:*

1. Duck

$\frac{1}{6}$ — Waddle
Costume $\frac{1}{2}$
Quack $\frac{1}{3}$

2. Cat

Purr $\frac{1}{8}$
Meow $\frac{1}{4}$
Scratch $\frac{1}{4}$
Costume $\frac{5}{8}$

3. Horse

$\frac{1}{6}$ — Neigh
Costume $\frac{5}{12}$
Run Fast $\frac{1}{6}$
Kick $\frac{1}{4}$

4. Cow

Eat Grass $\frac{1}{10}$
Chew Cud $\frac{1}{10}$
Costume $\frac{1}{2}$
Moo $\frac{3}{10}$

To accompany *Math Musicals,*
Newton & Descartes's Pet Center Adventure

Name _____

Newton is thinking of animals he can pretend to be. Fill in an animal name for the circle graphs in Exercises 3 and 4.

Then, for each circle graph:

a. write the missing fraction,

b. show that the sum of the fractions is 1, and

c. assign a characteristic of the animal to each part of the circle graph.

1. Duck

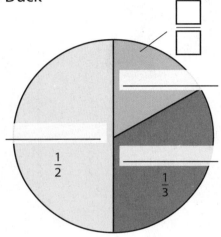

$\frac{1}{2}$ $\frac{1}{3}$

2. Cat

$\frac{1}{8}$ $\frac{1}{4}$ $\frac{1}{4}$

3. _____

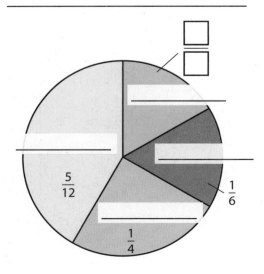

$\frac{5}{12}$ $\frac{1}{6}$ $\frac{1}{4}$

4. _____

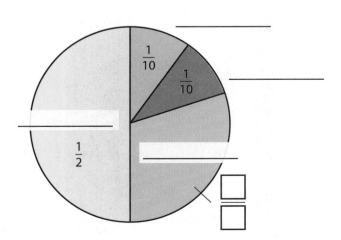

$\frac{1}{10}$ $\frac{1}{10}$ $\frac{1}{2}$

To accompany *Math Musicals,*
Newton & Descartes's Pet Center Adventure

Name _____

Newton is thinking of animals he can pretend to be. Fill in an animal name for the circle graphs in Exercises 3 and 4.

Then, for each circle graph:

a. write the missing fraction,

b. show that the sum of the fractions is 1, and

c. assign a characteristic of the animal to each part of the circle graph.

1. Duck

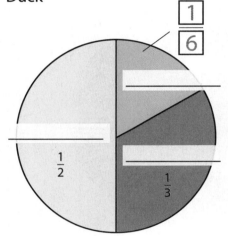

2. Cat

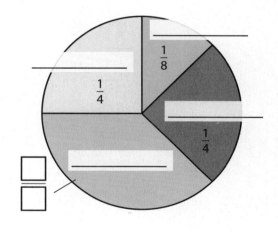

3. _____

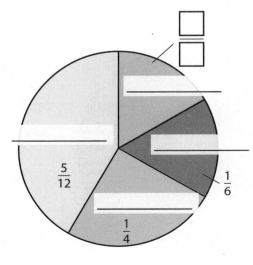

4. _____

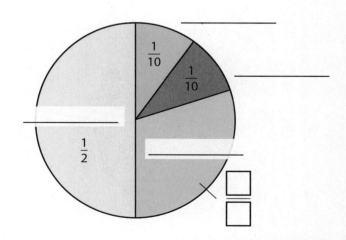

To accompany *Math Musicals,*
Newton & Descartes's Pet Center Adventure

Name _____

Newton is thinking of animals he can pretend to be. Fill in an animal name for the circle graphs in Exercises 3 and 4.

Then, for each circle graph:

a. write the missing fraction,

b. show that the sum of the fractions is 1, and

c. assign a characteristic of the animal to each part of the circle graph.

1. Duck

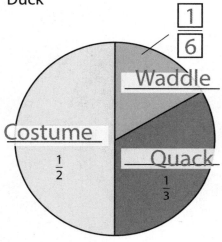

$\frac{1}{6}$ Waddle

Costume $\frac{1}{2}$ Quack $\frac{1}{3}$

2. Cat

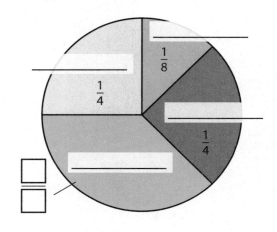

$\frac{1}{8}$

$\frac{1}{4}$

$\frac{1}{4}$

3. _____

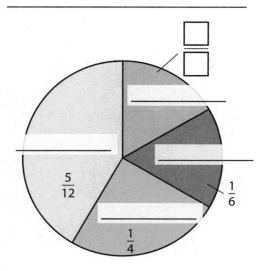

$\frac{5}{12}$ $\frac{1}{6}$

$\frac{1}{4}$

4. _____

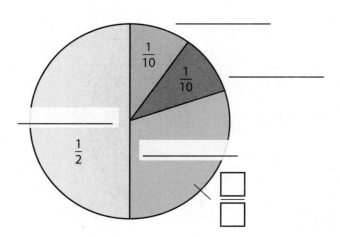

$\frac{1}{10}$

$\frac{1}{10}$

$\frac{1}{2}$

To accompany *Math Musicals,*
Newton & Descartes's Pet Center Adventure

Rich Math Task
Volume

This Rich Math Task extends student learning from finding the volumes of right rectangular prisms to finding missing dimensions and converting volumes to different units. Remind students of their previous work with measurement conversions. Review the importance of the unit in a measurement.

• Newton and Descartes's
: **Rich Math Tasks**

Name _____

In the final episode of *Newton and Descartes's Pet Center Adventure*, Descartes is challenged to a contest in the lap pool. His friend, Charlie, calculates the volume of the lap pool.

The table below shows the dimensions of several other pools.

Complete the table.

	Length	Width	Depth	Volume
1.	5 meters	2 meters	2 meters	**20 cu. ft**
2.	25 feet	20 feet	5 feet	**2,500 cu. ft**
3.	**10 meters**	4 meters	2 meters	80 cu. m
4.	6 yards	**4 yards**	$3\frac{1}{2}$ yards	84 cu. yd
5.	30 feet	8.5 feet	10 feet	**2,550 cu. ft**
6.	50 feet	20 feet	**2 feet**	2,000 cu. ft

1 cubic yard = 27 cubic feet   1 cubic meter = 35.3 cubic feet

7. Of the 6 pools in the table, which has the greatest volume?

#3 (2,824 cu. ft)

706 cu. ft
2,500 cu. ft
2,824 cu. ft
2,268 cu. ft
2,550 cu. ft
2,000 cu. ft

To accompany *Math Musicals,*
Newton & Descartes's Pet Center Adventure

Name _____

In the final episode of *Newton and Descartes's Pet Center Adventure*, Descartes is challenged to a contest in the lap pool. His friend, Charlie, calculates the volume of the lap pool.

The table below shows the dimensions of several other pools.

Complete the table.

	Length	Width	Depth	Volume
1.	5 meters	2 meters	2 meters	_____
2.	25 feet	20 feet	5 feet	_____
3.	_____	4 meters	2 meters	80 cu. m
4.	6 yards	_____	$3\frac{1}{2}$ yards	84 cu. yd
5.	30 feet	8.5 feet	10 feet	_____
6.	50 feet	20 feet	_____	2,000 cu. ft

1 cubic yard = 27 cubic feet   1 cubic meter = 35.3 cubic feet

7. Of the 6 pools in the table, which has the greatest volume? _____

To accompany *Math Musicals,*
Newton & Descartes's Pet Center Adventure

Name _____

In the final episode of *Newton and Descartes's Pet Center Adventure*, Descartes is challenged to a contest in the lap pool. His friend, Charlie, calculates the volume of the lap pool.

The table below shows the dimensions of several other pools.

Complete the table.

	Length	Width	Depth	Volume
1.	5 meters	2 meters	2 meters	_40 cu. m_
2.	25 feet	20 feet	5 feet	_____
3.	_____	4 meters	2 meters	80 cu. m
4.	6 yards	_____	$3\frac{1}{2}$ yards	84 cu. yd
5.	30 feet	8.5 feet	10 feet	_____
6.	50 feet	20 feet	_____	2,000 cu. ft

1 cubic yard = 27 cubic feet   1 cubic meter = 35.3 cubic feet

7. Of the 6 pools in the table, which has the greatest volume? _____

To accompany Math Musicals,
Newton & Descartes's Pet Center Adventure

Name _____

In the final episode of *Newton and Descartes's Pet Center Adventure*, Descartes is challenged to a contest in the lap pool. His friend, Charlie, calculates the volume of the lap pool.

The table below shows the dimensions of several other pools.

Complete the table.

	Length	**Width**	**Depth**	**Volume**
1.	5 meters	2 meters	2 meters	<u>40 cu. m</u>
2.	25 feet	20 feet	5 feet	_____
3.	<u>10 meters</u>	4 meters	2 meters	80 cu. m
4.	6 yards	_____	$3\frac{1}{2}$ yards	84 cu. yd
5.	30 feet	8.5 feet	10 feet	_____
6.	50 feet	20 feet	_____	2,000 cu. ft

1 cubic yard = 27 cubic feet   1 cubic meter = 35.3 cubic feet

7. Of the 6 pools in the table, which has the greatest volume? _____

To accompany *Math Musicals*,
Newton & Descartes's Pet Center Adventure